India

Red Lead .

My Favou

E

An Esse✂ Girl
on the
Costa
Blanca

To Blake.

Joanna Blackford (Joanna Downs) started off as a young single mother challenging anything that stepped in her way, taking on what she wanted out of life. Taught to believe in herself and to conquer the crises life presented to her. She's a hairdresser, salon manageress, English salon owner, Spanish salon owner, ex-Spanish bar owner, wife and mother of two.

And now she's a writer.

SHE WHO DARES WINS!

An Essex Girl
on the
Costa
Blanca

Jo Black

Brewster
Publishing

First published in June 2013
by Brewster Publications
122 Broad Walk, Hockley, Essex SS55DG
brewsterpublications@gmail.com
© Copyright Jo Black

A CIP catalogue reference for this book is available from the
British Library.

ISBN: 978-0-9576734-0-3

Cover illustration by Yasmin Walsh
Cover photograph by Kenneth Yendell
Cover and contents design and typeset by Señor Ken
Printed and bound in Great Britain

Acknowledgements

This book is faction, believe what you want to believe and enjoy.

Some of the characters used in this novel have been mashed up to protect their idiosyncrasies Whereas some characters are who they are and have nothing to hide, including my husband, Michael. Locations named are true in description, a perfect guide to the Costa Blanca. Denia takes its name from the Roman Goddess, Diana. Thank you to Derek Lambert's book, Spanish Lessons, for the inspiration. Heartfelt thanks to:

My husband, Michael, for putting up with me on yet another crazy challenge and for believing in me.

My daughter, Sarina who at times had to put her social life on hold, as well as being told to shhhhhhhhhhhhhhhhh.

My son, Louis for achieving his career.

My parents for supporting me and my son during his growing up.

My editor Sylvana, who took the challenge to edit an Essex girl.

Chrissie, for your help and advice in proof reading.

Betty for the final proof reading.

Yasmin, for the illustration of me, a great artist at only fifteen years of age.

Ken, for completely putting me together, as a book.

Margaret for encouraging me.

The Denia Writers Circle, for educating me and allowing me to stay, not that you had a choice.

Friends of the Children of Emaus

An Essex Girl on the Costa Blanca has been written to help raise money for Emaus childrens shelters (Friends of the Children of Emaus) and a percentage of sales of this book will go to to this charity.

There are 9 shelters in the Valencian Community in Spain occupied by nearly 120 children who have been taken into care because of unfortunate circumstances.

The shelters are funded with grants from the Generalitat of Valencia, but this is never enough to provide everything the children need. Each year they are short by 30% of their operating costs, so they rely on donations to make up the short fall.

Due to the crisis in Spain government money is failing to materialise and fewer people are able to fundraise. Friends of the Children of Emaus is struggling with simple, everyday outgoings such as food and electricity bills.

I am hoping the sales of this book can make a difference.

Jo Black x

Contents

* * *The departure* * *

It is May 2005. Fifty thousand pounds was being counted out from a Tesco carrier bag in the toilet of my hairdressing salon, which was the size of a shoebox. The notes were painstakingly laid out on a slatted chair in neat piles of fifties, carefully counted until one note went missing, lost between one of the wooden slats. Michael was clearly stressed; I'm sure his back ached as well as his behind from sitting for what was some time now on a cold toilet seat. But I wasn't worried about that.

'Is it all there? Haven't you counted it all yet?' I asked nervously as I peered through the small opening of the door.

My buyer had arrived unexpectedly half an hour ago, determined to cut the deal. 'Half the money, like you wanted. Take it now, or the sales off.' he had burst out with his Essex twang, as he entered the salon. At the time I was sitting at my reception desk, lost for words. With a thud the plastic carrier bag of money was dumped onto my desk. 'I've got us an appointment at four with me solicitor.' he had explained. Oh, I thought, I had obviously pushed this guy too far; this was something I

1

was very good at. There had been several disagreements concerning the contract his lawyer had drawn up.

'Okay, take a seat,' I had said. What else was there to say? Naturally and without hesitation I snatched up the money and placed it on top of my Gucci handbag for safekeeping.

Without delay he had then plonked himself down opposite me in my black faux-leather chair, arms folded like a triumphant stroppy child, staring directly at me, eyes possessed, similar to Jack Nicholson from *The Shining*. Luckily there were no clients or staff present.

He was a man of few words who hadn't won any charisma contests. He was buying the salon for his girlfriend, lucky cow, when I think how hard I've had to work to get to this stage. Now had finally lost patience with me; he'd had enough so he took an aggressive stance. Normally I am not pushed around by a guy of his character but in circumstances where business is concerned, cash is king.

At that very moment Michael had walked in through the door and acknowledged my buyer with a not-so-sure look. Relief then swept over my whole body. I hadn't told Michael of my buyer's pleasant personality; I didn't want anything to stop the sale. And now that he was here, he could count the money whilst I cut my last client's hair who was due any minute. I stood up from my chair and strolled over to my husband, greeted him with a kiss, then whispered into his ear. 'Michael, he's brought me half the cash like I wanted and I'm to get the rest at four when we meet with the solicitor. Just take it to the toilet and check it's all there.'

I had handed him the Tesco carrier bag which he'd looked at in disbelief and said, 'I only came in for a quick coffee.'

'Just get on with it before one of the girls notices, you can count it in the toilet.' I sternly whispered under my breath as I glanced towards the buyer from the corner of my eye.

Most of the cash had now been counted from what I could see. Michael looked up anxiously from the toilet seat and snapped.

'Shit! If I miscount, Jo, I know you'll kill me.' He reached down to the tiled floor to retrieve the lost note. I left him to it and returned to my client who was now putting on her coat and admiring her new haircut in the mirror.

'How much do I owe you?' she asked.

'Twenty-five pounds, please.'

'Well good luck in your new adventure, I'll miss you. You've cut my hair for a long time, Jo. I hope I can find someone who can cut as good as you.'

'Ah, thank you, you will. I'll miss you too.' We hugged and she left. Another goodbye to a long-term client, the last one to be told.

Once she had left I cashed up the till. My staff was busying themselves, oblivious of what was going on. I was selling the salon secretly, so as not to unsettle the employees, which consisted of 3 girls, 2 stylists and a beautician. I was to let them know later that day, although I suspect they were aware of the sale.

Michael tied the carrier bag into a knot and left the salon toilet. He approached me hesitantly, looking around for suspicious staff. Not that it mattered at this point; if they wanted to leave, let them - I was now one step closer to the completion of sale.

'So, is it all there?' I asked, while I swept up the remains of my last haircut. I nervously looked across the room towards my buyer who was still sitting in my reception area, flicking through a magazine.

'Yes of course.' Michael looked tired as sweat beaded his forehead. He wiped it dry with a neatly folded handkerchief taken from his trouser pocket. Excitement ran through me.

It was now nearly 3.30 pm. I rushed around the salon to check everything was as it should be, and nervously grabbed what I could: cutting tools, hairdryer and some extra stock. *Fuck' it,* I thought. *No one will notice what was taken.*

'Do you want me to carry anything?' Michael asked.

'No, it's alright. Let's go. We'll stop off at dad's first and leave him with this half of the cash.'

All three of us left at that point. My father lived only five minutes from the salon. He had suffered a catastrophic stroke a year previously. He now uses the reserve part of his brain that few of us need or know about. Sadly he can't talk, apart from the F-word, frequently and loosely bandied about, and he has little use of his right arm. Other than that he's a good candidate to leave the money with, sure to be safe. Naturally I was anxious, worried about being mugged with fifty grand in a Tesco carrier bag or maybe the taxman awaited me at the solicitors. After experiencing two tax investigations, anything was possible. My imagination began to run wild.

Just as we approached the driveway, there was dad by his front door, always a man on time. I ran over with the cash; he snatched from me as soon as my foot reached his doorstep and giving me a cheeky smirk of approval, he then slammed the front door shut in my face. I stood gob-smacked.

'I guess you still haven't lost your sense of humour dad.' With that we left to collect the remainder of the money. I think at the time my dad sat on the cash. I also wondered whether the solicitor had placed the rest of the money into a Safeway carrier bag.

The solicitor's office was just around the corner from where my father lived. It was an ageing practice that smelled musty as you entered. I believed they should have put this man out to grass a long time ago but nevertheless he was holding the rest of my cash, so who gave a shite. Take the money and run. Oh, and most importantly, of course, sign the contracts.

'Take a seat, Mrs Blackbird,' he announced as we entered his office and pointed towards two stained moth-bitten office chairs.

'No, sorry, my name's Blackford.' You'd have thought he would have known my name, especially as he'd drawn up the contracts. Naturally I had sought my legal advice elsewhere.

'Here we are. I do believe this belongs to you.' The solicitor handed me a large brown envelope of cash that I then passed to Michael. I was far too nervous to count the money. The contents of the contract were of more interest. I was armed with a few questions ready to fire, although my queries were answered in an incomprehensible manner. I just agreed and signed the paperwork as it was handed to me. Who cared, I was going to live in Spain. Mission accomplished. Signed and sealed. My hair and beauty salon of ten years was now sold. A mistake, or was it?

* * *Cuts 'N' Curls Hair & Beauty* * *

I had started the business at the age of twenty-five, after leaving a position as manageress.

Six days a week I worked, a single mum bringing up my son Louis with the support from my family. The business grew from one small hairdressing salon to expand next door making it two shops which offered beauty treatments as well as giving me extra cutting space and more staff, bringing with it the invariable headaches connected with the strict employment laws; but a profitable move. My salon was located in a very small village, Ashingdon, just ten minutes from Southend, within the countryside of Essex. It consisted of one pub, a primary school and a few odd shops. If you held your breath for 40 seconds, you could drive the length of the village from one end to the other. Not recommended on a school morning.

I came upon the shop purely by accident while on route to horse riding one Sunday morning. I was feeling a little nauseous from the previous night's consumption of too much alcohol with my childhood friend Sharon. Horse riding is a good natural hangover cure, it charges up the adrenalin and takes your mind off how you really feel. We drove up the steep Ashingdon hill and passed an assortment of horses grazing in the nearby field just off the country road. Celine Dion blared out whilst Sharon drove aimlessly with my navigation. We confabulated about a plan of action for 'my future' as we reached the top of the hill on a road I was very familiar with. I suddenly noticed some buildings being restored and the image of a hair salon that had always been in my thoughts for this particular area came to mind. Now an opportunity was arising and presenting itself.

'Stop' I shouted. 'Look, they're building new shops.' Sharon then pulled over into the layby. We noticed the builder just inside one of the properties, so, without hesitation, we jumped out of the car and walked over to question him. Conveniently, he was also the landlord.

'Are these gonna be shops?' I asked.

'Hello. Yes, four shops with only two left for rent,' he replied.

'How much are they to rent and which ones are left?' A hundred questions later this poor man must have thought I was the Gestapo. A handsome, middle-aged man, kind; he offered me good advice.

I desperately needed to do something with my life: I had married a man for wealth and security and no longer saw a future with him. I did not love him and consequently this led to divorce. I now needed a new home and a profitable business to support my son and me.

So there it was: a solution to my problem. A hairdressing salon with accommodation above it for rent. This all fell into place. It was meant to be.

Ten years later, a successful business was established. It was now time to move on to the next challenge in my life. My father calls me, 'the woman of substance.' But here we were about to cut off the best income I ever had for a new life in Spain...

* * Searching for a future business in Spain * *

Our dream was to buy a bar in Denia, a job easy enough for anyone to do, with little or no qualifications required. Denia, the jewel of the Costa Blanca, on the Northern Coast, offers the best beaches, vast mountains and citrus groves as well. It is a historic fishing village that has been modernised and restructured, very cosmopolitan but still very Spanish. To buy a bar would be part of our future business plan and in our thoughts we were hoping it would give us an income straight away, enough to pay our mortgage and bills, especially for the first two to three years. During this time, we also planned to network for mobile hair clients and to meet as many locals as possible, so that we would eventually open the first English hair and beauty salon in Denia. The interval would give me time with our three–year-old daughter, and would help to settle us both into Spanish school: Sarina as a pupil and me as a foreign mother. Michael, my husband, now became the breadwinner. I no longer wanted to be the 'woman of substance'. I wanted family life and only part time work in a bar with no responsibility. So I could become a *'yummy mummy'*.

On the internet one evening, a month before we departed the UK to start our new lives in Spain, I had seen a bar for sale. We had been in search of a bar for a few months and nothing had been available until now. I recognised the address of the bar, it was situated exactly where I had wanted, in a busy parade of shops and bars, with a large popular supermarket and most importantly, plenty of parking. Michael, who had been out to play badminton, returned home to discover that he was on a flight to Spain the very next day to view this bar. So he took a 'sickie' from work for two days. He knew the bar instantly and warned me it wasn't what we wanted. I didn't listen; as far as I was concerned it was in exactly the position I wanted.

* * *Buying the bar* * *

There it stood. Andrew's Bar in 2005 was a dirty, shabby, rundown bar but perfectly situated along Las Marinas, the beach road from Denia to Els Poblets. The bar was set between other bars, restaurants and a supermarket, with a two-minute walk to the beach opposite, and a view which looked on to a row of palm trees.

During the day the bar was used by holiday makers, that is, when it was open. Of a night, I think it was abused by drunkards and druggies most of the time, intermingled with a few civilised locals and holiday makers. What a challenge!

Michael flew to Spain that morning. I called his office to let them know he was sick. He met the agent, Dave, a tall man with a moustache who perspired giving off a strong smell of *Kouros* and who sounded like a typical car salesman: not to be trusted. So he was in the perfect job: a con man who sold properties and businesses. He wanted only thirty thousand euros for the traspaso (fixtures and fittings and good will) plus twelve thousand euros commission for himself. Of course, after lots of negotiation and several stern phone calls from me, we didn't pay him these amounts, although he still wangled for half the commission. Being naïve and green in a new country, this was the first lesson we learned; not to trust your fellow countryman was the second. The bar was owned by a Frenchman who wanted to secretly sell the lease behind his son's back, Andrew, who was a tall, skinny, fair- haired, likeable chap but just too young to run a bar, even though he'd given it his best shot. This secrecy was the reason we had to deal with the car salesman. The saying 'don't have family work for you' was sadly true in this case. We had several meetings with our newly appointed solicitor who advised Michael not to pay the asking price and also informed us about other bars for rent at a cheaper price. Naturally I followed my instinct and chose to ignore the advice given. I was in a rush to start our new lives. Michael, meanwhile, felt hesitant about the whole situation. He had a vague image of the bar before viewing it, which wasn't a positive one; he warned me to first view it before he put a deposit down. 'No Michael, I don't want to wait, just leave a 5,000 euro deposit. We can decorate it, it can't be that bad.' I wasn't listening to his views; I was more interested in its position, the price and the timing of the sale. Michael wasn't a gambler in life, as I was. He had been happy with his new promotion and was unsure of my dream. Consequently after lots of convincing, he left a deposit and flew back.

During this quick visit to Denia Michael was able to

stay in our new house, which had been completed earlier that year. After two years of construction fraught with lies, finally, our house was built. This gave us a little peace of mind knowing that we had now found a business to support us in a popular tourist area with lots of passing trade. Location, location, location. It was also within our price range. I was convinced, with my English naivety, that we had found the perfect business. So we were now ready to begin our new lives!

Michael had recently handed his notice in at work reluctantly. This was a difficult decision for him as at the beginning of the year he had just received a promotion to area sales manager within the tool distribution company where he worked. The promotion meant more money, a new company car every six months, free mobile phone and private health insurance, etc. This was a position he had longed for and had worked hard towards. All this was to be exchanged for work in a bar and to wear espadrilles, shorts, T-shirt, to mop up people's slops, deal with drunks, finish at five in the morning, not to mention his 'company' scooter instead of a prestige car for transport. I thought this was a fair enough exchange, although he didn't seem to agree, given he thought he had always looked good in a suit. Michael is a handsome man: highlighted hair, piercing blue eyes and yes, a Burt Lancaster smile with those white straight teeth that gleamed. These were the features that attracted me to Michael that very first day when we met.

* * *I'm in love* * *

At the time I had been a single mum for 9 years, in and
out of short relationships, Fussy wasn't the word for it. I
was looking for a man that stood his ground with me. A
man that wore one trouser leg, so I could wear the other;
I was bored of wearing both. Also there was my 11 year-
old son Louis to consider. I was successfully running the
hair and beauty salon in Ashingdon. My accountant was
advising me to spend some money on advertising, 'Why
don't you sponsor a football team?' he said jokingly, 'tax
deductible, also, while you're at it, you might find
yourself a husband.' Now that was an idea! I had a friend,
Gary, who ran the Ashingdon football club, and I just so
happened to cut his hair; he was keen on the idea so we
arranged to meet at the local pub one Sunday after a
match.

On the day I felt a little apprehensive especially
when I entered the pub alone; I met Gary as I walked in
which made me feel a little more comfortable. It was a
man's pub, apart from the bar maid I was the only female.
Gary was the manager of the team and we had been

friends for years, since our teens. He was tall, skinny and possessed a rather large Adam's apple.

'Would you like a drink?'

'Of course, Chardonnay please.' I sat down and checked out the environment to see if any of my clients were here; I only spotted one. Gary eventually arrived with my Chardonnay then several minutes later, this handsome, drop-dead gorgeous guy appeared who joined us without any introduction. I just had to ask 'And who are you?'

'Michael, I'm the other manager.' I looked for a wedding ring, there wasn't one. We chatted for an hour about football kits and the benefits I would receive as a sponsor. This length of time was enough time to drink my wine and fall in love with a guy I knew nothing about. I returned home, telephoned my mum and told her, 'I am in love - I don't care if he's married, engaged or has ten kids, whatever, I am in love.' At the time I'm sure my mum had thought: Here we go again, Jo's never been in love, and took the conversation with a pinch of salt.

Several weeks passed and the team was having a Saturday night out in Southend at one of the Night clubs to which I was invited along with some friends. I was excited to meet this guy Michael again; sadly though, as we arrived, there was Michael with another girl, Shelley, blonde and attractive (when seen in the dark); he was snogging her or she was snogging him. I thought this was his girlfriend but later found out she wasn't and discovered that he was living with another girl who obviously wasn't there that night. What a slug! My friends were not impressed with this guy when I told them about him; they dismissed him straight away and strongly advised me to stay away. The evening became a long night and I just wanted to go home. I was gutted.

The very next day both Gary and Michael were to meet at my house in Ashingdon, a modern 3-bed semi-detached I'd recently purchased. I had worked hard as a single mother and now 30 years old I was climbing the ladder at a good pace. Michael looked very sheepish as he entered my kitchen that day. We all had coffee and I commented on his drunken state from the previous night. Then I asked, 'Who was that girl you were sucking face with'? I couldn't help myself.

'Oh some girl.' He was embarrassed and changed the subject. We then discussed the football kits I was to purchase and the logo 'Cuts N Curls'. Michael knew a company that sold kits and would do the sign writing.

'Is it just the home kit you want to sponsor'? God yes! I wasn't made of money; one kit was enough to sponsor. I was still attracted to this Casanova but chose to ignore how I felt. I knew my heart was at risk of getting broken and this I wanted to protect. As the boys were about to leave, Michael asked, 'When will our next meeting be?' I brushed him away, to show him I was far too good for him.

'When you have the art work call me for an

appointment'. He looked disappointed, his ego had been blown, and they then left.

We had several meetings discussing the kit, the colours and finance; when one particular meeting at my house after several cups of coffee, an intense discussion on our private lives and an immense amount of flirting; Michael just couldn't help himself and asked me out. 'Of course not. You have a girlfriend with whom you live. When you separate I'll consider a date,' and then I assured him that I wasn't into sharing!

Six months passed, during which our meetings became more regular as were the offers for a date. I refused each and every one until one afternoon I was out shopping in a supermarket and bumped into a friend. She asked if I had given into Michael's offers of dating. She suggested I should take him up on his offer as he was never going to split from his girlfriend just for a date with me that may turn out a disaster and that may result in me not liking him after all or he may not like me. So I re-thought the situation, and just as I was about to call him to arrange a date, the phone rang. 'Hi, its Michael, I forgot to thank you for the coffee the other day.'

'Oh yes, coffee, that's OK,' (*feeble excuse for a chat*, I thought), 'I was going to call to see if that offer for a drink still stands?'

'Yeh, sure, when do you want to meet?'

We agreed to meet for a drink in Strawberry fields, a restaurant pub, modern, comfortably furnished and only 10 minutes' drive from my house. It was perfect for a secret date where neither of us could be recognised. The evening was a great success, and what I feared most happened-falling for this guy and leaving my heart unprotected. We laughed all night, in fact so much so that afterwards both our cheeks hurt. We had both fallen for each other. How was I to handle this situation? He was still living with another girl and what if he didn't want to leave her? These thoughts were constantly on my mind. Regardless I couldn't help myself. We were constantly texting each other and having several more dates. Michael's girlfriend eventually sussed the situation. She knew something was going on, and there was upset all round. I never did meet her, but I felt her pain because I knew how I would have felt if I was on the receiving end. He chose to leave her after several weeks of turmoil and somehow, unintentionally, moved in with Louis and me. This was a quick decision for both of us, but we knew it was right, it felt right. We became inseparable; it was as if we were made for one another, we shared the same thoughts and had similar behaviour (which wasn't always a good thing); at times we clashed but we grew to understand one another. Five months went by when surprisingly we both decided to have a baby. This thought had never crossed my mind, as by then Louis was 11 years old. This would be a large age gap for his sibling, but I had now found long-term love and wanted to have his baby even though I was now 31 years old.

Previously, Michael had never wanted children but his feelings were the same as mine. So on February 5, 2002 Sarina Maria was born.

Shit happened. Our lives took a dramatic change. Problems occurred at the salon when a member of staff ran off with a quarter of my clientele, god bless her. My blood pressure boiled over as did my anxiety and financially I was in trouble. Oh not to mention my son was going through puberty. Michael verged on mid-life crisis as well, and on top of that there was a wedding to be organised. I had just given birth, post-natal depression had only just settled in. Happy homes! So I got right back into the saddle by taking lots of deep breaths and exercising and tackled each problem one at a time.

I was beginning to regret the business. Sadly, Sarina had to attend crèche from the age of three months, for four days a week, whilst in between time Donna and Regan babysat her in their florist shop, which was only 2 doors along from the salon. Donna had started her business roughly at the same time as me and Regan was her assistant. We had formed a great relationship through the years, supporting each other. The girls were like sisters to one another, Regan a bit of a tomboy and Donna a real mother hen who listened to everyone's problems.

I nurtured Michael and guided him into family life which wasn't easy and still isn't easy to this day. And Louis survived puberty.

In the hairdressing trade there's always the threat of someone wanting a piece of one's action and I didn't like to share what I had worked so hard for, especially since I had become a single mother. It was this threat that became one of the many reasons we decided to move to Spain, the risk of another staff member building a clientele from within one's own business to then take it from you at one's own cost always existed. Another reason was our need to have quality time with our daughter, we wanted to watch her grow and be able to collect her ourselves from kindergarten or school. This an option was not available if we had stayed in England; our jobs worked us long hours to only just keep up with the rat race. We wanted an easier life in the sun that wouldn't cost too much, a simple home life without the material things, and with low overheads. Living the dream! Well so we thought!

* * *Leaving England for Spain for good* * *

The time had finally arrived and here we were packing
and selling off our last unwanted furniture. Michael had
recently returned from Spain, re-considering what he
had done; the whole project disturbed him and then
there was the deposit he had put down on a bar that I
hadn't seen and knew I wouldn't like. Was it wise, was it
going to be good enough, was it going to work? Of course
it was I assured him. He was troubled, I was excited,
nothing was going to stop me and he knew that. So he
put the thought out of his mind and carried on working
his notice at work. I had packed most of the boxes and
had only the leather suite to sell, which soon sold after
I'd advertised it in the local newspaper. It was only a year
old, cream leather in perfect condition. Until my darling
three year old daughter decided to paint her toe nails on
it. She had sat on the arm of the chair and took several
long strokes of my reddest nail polish, proceeded to paint
not only her minute toe nails but carried the long strokes
of polish onto my leather suite, after which she was bored
and dropped the rest of the polish down the inside of it.
It seemed such a short time that I had taken my eyes off

her. Now I was faced with the dread of the buyer coming that day. I wasn't sure what frightened me the most - removing the bright red stain of polish or being able to achieve this within the following two hours, before the buyer arrived. Acetone saved both Sarina and me.

The ensuing two weeks soon passed. I organised everything from a removal lorry to car transport, bartered for the best price with several known companies then finalised all the necessary paper work and payment of all utility bills due on the house we had been renting for the past six months and set up a re-direction for our post. There is so much to organise and finalise when leaving your home country.

* * The arrival * *

Stansted Airport, at four in the morning, my nerves were bad; I was apprehensive about the flight and the journey ahead of us. Sarina, in her pyjamas, sat wide-awake in her pushchair with her *Tweenies* bag clutched tight to her chest. I wondered if she knew I had put a few thousand pounds into it. Oh well, I had to get this cash over to Spain somehow.

'Sarina, don't get out, especially with that bag. Stay in your pushchair, darling.' Was I concerned about Sarina or the money she was carrying? Each of us carried some of the money. I had traveller's cheques as well. Even my mother in-law, April, was carrying some of the cash because she had offered to hold our flight bag. If only she knew, she probably would have run off with it and caught the next flight to Vegas. So yes, my mother- in-law, a short, greyish lady in her sixties who due to ill health, sadly looked a little older, was to join us for six weeks to help settle the Blackford family. Louis stayed behind as he still had a couple of exams to finish but he was to join us in June. His was to be a temporary visit, as he'd made it clear enough that he wasn't going to stay permanently with us preferring to live in England. Leaving our son was very difficult. He didn't share the same dream as we hoped; he wanted to stay amongst his friends and family. He now lived with my mother and visited my father (my parents were separated); Louis kept a bond between both my parents quite amicably. He was now almost sixteen and wanted to pursue his career in carpentry. Sadly, we understood this was for the best as it was his future we had to consider; also his not speaking Spanish was one large disadvantage and being dyslexic was another. So an apprenticeship enabling him to learn a trade was more beneficial for his future. It was a sacrifice I had to accept.

The flight was a comfortable one, especially after several chardonnays, a couple of vodkas, an OK magazine and duty free. Once we landed, my nervousness returned because our lives were about to change dramatically: I had forced Michael to put a deposit down on a bar that I hadn't yet seen, there was so much to take in and I prayed I'd not made a mistake!

May, a perfect month to arrive; I felt the heat as I stepped off the plane as well as butterflies fluttering in my tummy. We had an appointment that same day for me to visit the bar. My dream had begun. 'Michael, we'll get our cases, while you get the hire car, babe.' We flew through customs, luckily no one checked us; mission 1 was completed: getting the cash out of the country without being robbed!

Within an hour and a half we were at the bar. It was closed; all I could see was a terrace with a few cigarette butts and a grey rusty shutter pulled down. We waited outside in the hire car for Dave, the car salesman. Sarina had drifted off to sleep during the journey so helped us view the bar in peace; April stayed behind with her. 'Here they are.' Michael said, as he opened the car door.

'Will you be ok April for a minute while I take a look at our new investment?' I asked, observing the two men shaking Michael's hand.

'Yeah we're, fine go ahead, I'd have liked to see it, but I can look later.'

Was she being funny? I asked myself, but dismissed her reply. Michael introduced me to Dave, the slippery character with a moustache, then to Andrew, the bar owner's son who now was obviously aware of the sale? His vacation was soon to be over so he would have to get another job working for someone else. Andrew pulled up the shutter, which rattled with age. There it was – dark, dingy and cold. *I'm from Essex, get me out of here. Is this my first thought?* I looked over at Michael, he saw my disappointment instantly.

'It's fine babe.' I said half-heartedly, what else was there to say standing there in shock. We had already put down a 5,000 euro deposit, and it was too late to change our minds. Decorate I thought, reforming was what this bar needed. The only thing I could think that was missing was the spit and saw dust. What were we buying? We didn't have the money to reform. As I was shown around and the more I saw my heart sank deeper and deeper.

'You wanted me to put the deposit down, Jo.' Michael urged, once we were alone in the kitchen.

'I know, I know, but its crap, it's small. It'll be fine, once we clean and decorate it.' I convinced myself. Michael had warned me. *New furniture would help* was my first positive thought. We were here now and mission 2 was still incomplete. Not one of my best business moves. We'll wait to meet the punters; - that will help. We left without showing April; I needed a drink to get over my shock.

Time passed quickly; there was a lot to organise and learn, and we only had one week to complete all the necessary documentation before completion. My mother in-law proved to be a problem: she was unhappy staying with us. Normally back home in England she had always been supportive and willing when asked to babysit. We hoped this would be her main role, to release the pressure off us both so we could get the business set up together. Sadly, this didn't happen. She only lasted three weeks in Spain. I think at the time it was because she had been taken away from her normal, natural environment and missed the rest of her family. Also she didn't like the food or the heat. For the first two weeks, we ate out a lot. Understandably, we were in a holiday spirit, whilst we were finalising the bar. Steak in Spain is cooked very rare, even well done resembles that of medium as we know it. Naturally that's what April ate: steak, which on one occasion she shoved to the middle of the table with a 'yuk.' I guess that meant she didn't like it. Being of an older mind set she reminded me a little of my nanny Rose, in her ways very old-fashioned and one who doesn't accept change very easily. She would only eat red meat, veg, salad and chocolate. Michael searched for an English shop to buy some food to satisfy his mother, but choice was very limited in Denia, especially as we were new to the area and there was only one shop that we knew of that sold English produce.

All this was an additional stress for me. I had no baby-sitter as April clearly wasn't offering her services, leaving Michael to set up the bar and decorate alone. She was unhappy and made this perfectly clear. So a bad atmosphere was set in the house that upset me and unsettled Sarina. I mean, let's face it we'd just moved to Spain, and were in negotiations to buy a bar, as well as organising Sarina's Spanish kindergarten. Furthermore, we had to wait for our furniture to arrive, let alone my convertible Beetle. How crazy was all that? And to top it all, we were building a new patio outside the front of our house, constructed by a guy called Wilson from Peru who only turned up for work when he thought it convenient, so, of course, I was nearing a nervous breakdown. Why didn't April understand? Adding to all this, my dad and his partner were also en route to stay with us for a week's holiday. This I was excited about, but also a little apprehensive, because of April's behaviour. I had seen a side of her that I hadn't seen before. She wore an upside down smile most days, and I couldn't change this, unless I physically turned her upside down to a handstand, then she would smile. Conversation between us became very limited. Most evenings I would sit outside with a book and a bottle of wine, enjoying the last part of sunshine and listen to the crickets churn.

I looked forward to my father's arrival. After his stroke, we were told Dad would only be with us for a couple of years as half his brain had died. Ten years later he still lives on, a very determined man. Naturally, I wanted my father and his partner, Donna, to see my vision. When they arrived, they were no problem, and fitted around our business schedule and April. They were relaxed and enjoyed the excitement of us buying a bar, especially when they received an invitation to Andrew's leaving do. A couple of times during their holiday Dad growled at April. Thankfully, he couldn't speak. I wonder what he would have said. Even with Dad's disabilities, he fitted in well with the locals. He almost sounded French as he spoke, not making any sense at all and still threw in the odd 'fucky woo'! Donna had become quite accustomed to this. Donna is quite reserved and sensitive; she is nearly half my dad's junior but what the hell. They love and care for one another and she had supported him during that dreadful time of his stroke.

* * Dad's stroke, flash back * *

It had been Good Friday when we received that fatal call. At work I was in deep conversation whilst cutting hair, when my colleague handed me the phone and urged I take the call. It was my sister who was very distressed.

'It's Dad. He's had a stroke and he's in Colchester hospital.'

Emotional shock hit me. *Focus and finish the cut and keep it together,* I told myself. Then I left the salon abruptly to collect both my children as quickly as possible. On arrival at Sarina's nursery I broke down and fell into floods of tears. There was no time for compassion. I then left urgently, not thinking straight to collect Louis from home and prepared myself for the drive ahead. Colchester hospital was at my driveable pace over an hour's drive away if not more, and it was Easter weekend so there was holiday traffic to be considered. My nerves were on edge, upset filled my entire body. My thoughts kept flooding in: the signs of a stroke had presented themselves to me only recently. If only I had said to Dad, 'Stop drinking and lose weight.' Would he have listened? Probably not.

That weekend we had already arranged family and friends to meet in Clacton. My father and I both owned static caravans there, so accommodation was organised between us. Dad had already arrived at his site and had just settled down with a glass of red wine when he suddenly suffered the stroke. An ambulance was called by Donna but it had rained all that day which caused delays for the ambulance crew to arrive and transport him to hospital. After a couple of hours in mud and misdirection, Dad had eventually made it to casualty unaware of what had gone on. I eventually arrived at the hospital after meeting Michael on route. My sister and her husband were already there to meet us. Dad waited in the observation ward. He looked dazed, not himself. Half his face had dropped, his eyes were rolling, not focused. I knew then something bad had happened or was going to happen, yet five hours had passed and still we were none the wiser.

The hospital was very busy; we all sat patiently in the waiting room. My sister Sarah and I comforted each other, as we always had since we were kids. Sarah is a year younger than me, yet behaves more maturely. Both our personalities couldn't be more different. I was the wild card, whilst Sarah was the sensible one.

'Stroke, what's a stroke?' No one could answer me; in medical terminology none of us knew what a stroke was. *How's it caused, will he be OK?* We were all left with those questions in our heads as the night had drawn on.

'It's late. I can stay with Dad, and you can come back tomorrow,' Donna suggested. Life can be so taken for granted. *Is this a testing ground for us or a teaching?* I asked myself. That Easter weekend left my family with a decision none of us wanted to make. Dad had suffered a catastrophic stroke and it was possible his heart could stop. *Do we resuscitate?* Dad's brain was already damaged, how much more could it take if his heart stopped. *Do we let nature take him or do we bring him back? But what if he is a vegetable?* Decisions were to be made. The doctors had told us he would have to live in a hospice and never walk again because of the severity of the stroke. They also warned us that he only had a 3 per cent chance of survival. Usually after such a stroke people don't survive.

Ray Downs never ran away from anything in his life. He was a survivor and a true believer. Had we all forgotten this? My brother, Darren, reminded me during a late night phone call that dad was a gambling man and so he gambled that 3 per cent! He taught himself to control his vital organs and body starting all over again like a baby. He strengthened each part of his body gradually over time. First Dad learned to swallow with a thickening powder that was put in his hot and cold drinks; this slowed the flow of liquid as he swallowed. He then had to retrain his bladder and learn to move his limbs. This took sheer determination. To stand and hold his own weight was the biggest test; to begin with he learnt to shuffle in step which soon enabled him to conquer his walk. 'The Bionic Man'.

Now having my father with me in Spain brought back the excitement of adventure. Here he was attending Andrew's leaving do after all that had happened to him. I left early with Sarina, while Michael, Donna and my dad stayed behind. They seemed to have a good time and Dad returned home wearing an *Andrew's Café Bar* T-shirt whereas Donna wasn't feeling too good and christened our half- laid patio. As for Michael, he couldn't remember much of the evening, only that he had met loads of people and couldn't remember any of their names. I wished I could have stayed with them at the bar but there was Sarina as well as Michael's mum to consider. The rest of their break was taken up with sunbathing, relaxing and eating out. They enjoyed their vacation and left with a tan and a bottle of *Ponche*, a brandy liqueur the local Spanish drink.

Michael learned the ropes of the bar with Andrew explaining. He taught Michael the same way he had been taught by Greta, the previous owner. Andrew got totally pissed while Michael was thrown in at the deep end and worked for nothing. He served Andrew and his customers all weekend, while at the same time abused; in time Michael would soon return this compliment. He had to learn the large measures of spirits to be poured onto the top of the second ice cube, pour a pint or a Cana (small beer) and work the coffee machine; he then had to learn all the Spanish names for coffee as well as the tab system and how to lock up the bar.

Ten days after we arrived, Andrew's father had arrived to sign contracts. His English wasn't good so we found ourselves dealing mainly with his representative, Annette. (Obviously he didn't care too much for the car salesman.) In fact we struck up a very good relationship with her; a drinking relationship. She owned an insurance company in Denia passed down by her father. A very laid-back kind of girl, dressed casually like a tom boy, who went everywhere with her boxer dog, Gomish; she conducted most of her business in bars while her PA dealt with the policies in her office. This proved to be a good working relationship. So there we were, about to deposit a large amount of cash into Andrew's father's safe-deposit box at a bank along the Marques de Campo, with Annette as our bodyguard and adviser. Contracts were later signed in her office. This then made us the new proud owners of Andrew's café bar.

* * Finding our Spanish house * *

Two years previously, in the January 2003, Michael and Leonard, his beer buddy, had first visited Denia on a free inspection trip through an estate agent in England. Michael had described the trip in great detail during several phone calls; I could picture myself being there with them. They had arrived in glorious sunshine. Ron, the estate agent, picked them up at Alicante airport meeting them under the green cross, the symbol throughout Spain for a pharmacy. A man of many talents, Ron spoke several languages. Naturally, he was Dutch. He had lived in Spain since his teens. Michael was quite taken with him and described him as a well-dressed gentleman in his early thirties, slim with a pleasant nature, and wore dark rimmed glasses.

They left the airport and drove along the AP7 motorway to Denia, taking in the scenery of Eastern Spain. Michael described Alicante as flat desert land, nothing scenic apart from the crystal blue sea, only motorway and concrete buildings. They travelled towards northern Costa Blanca. He labelled Benidorm as a concrete jungle, totally built up with high-rise hotels, a city of its own. Vegas, the land of make believe. Visit the city of Benidorm and become whatever you want: single, crazy, another sex, a drunkard disorderly, or even a sex machine. Or just relax and sit back with a euro pint of beer and watch the ghastly display of humans of all ages, not necessarily young, having fun, baring half their tattooed bodies.

Eventually they arrived at the last set of tolls. During their journey, Michael had asked lots of questions about the weather, property prices, and most importantly, where were they staying?

He described Ron as a walking encyclopaedia on Denia, and not a pushy estate agent.

Marques de Campo was their first port of call. After driving in and around narrow cobbled streets, they had eventually arrived at the heart of Denia. Now this was a picture postcard worth seeing describing it as a very long street overhung with the branches of beautiful plane trees on both sides of the road in front of shops, tapas bars, restaurants and boutiques.

Michael was totally taken with Denia and all it offered. The sun shone their whole weekend. They stopped for tapas and drinks, and relaxed in the sun for a short while to absorb this cosmopolitan city before their next instalment, the fabulous harbour. If the Campo didn't seal a sale, the harbour would be sure to!

The harbour is only a short distance away from the city of Denia. At this stage the shops and restaurants were still being built but luxury yachts were already harboured there, so Ron had to fill them in with the future construction plans. They walked along a newly built brick path, taking in the luxury view of well-kept yachts, worth thousands to millions of pounds, each flying their own country's flag. The larger yachts were recognisable mainly by their French flags. Hotels on water, pure luxury was found on this harbour. No expense spared. It was empty, not a soul to be seen. It was siesta time Michael had said. There was only the sound of the surf and the whistling wind that chimed, crashing waves that left foam of froth and seaweed on the rocks and boulders. Construction was heavily in process for the soon-to-be shops and restaurants all with increasingly high rentals. It all seemed so unreal.

The boys wanted time for more drinkies and possibly a football match on TV. So Ron had to accommodate; beer wasn't his first love (like these lads had in mind), and football, well I guess he had to grin and bear it, especially if it meant a sale. They went to Andrew's bar, (as fate, would have it), little did Michael know that two years hence he would own this very café bar. It was a man's bar and not the poshest but it had English football.

The rest of their weekend was then taken up with property viewings, no pressure applied; the only pressure was put on Ron, to drink lots of beer. These were Essex boys, after all and Leonard had to be fed and watered at regular intervals whereas Michael only needed watering.

Leonard is a lot younger than Michael. They had met playing football and drinking at the same local, and going on an 18-30s holiday, where Michael had lent Leonard half his wardrobe due to his lack of funds. Now a computer whiz in London, the roles are reversed. They both share the same interests, beer and football, even though there is a fifteen-year age gap, they are mates with the same interests.

During this inspection trip, Michael had been shown two properties that he thought I may like, both, being new builds. One was already built and the other was off-plan, due to be completed in a year's time, hopefully.

Michael returned very impressed with the area that had been recommended by our neighbour Madge, who had recently sold her UK property to retire there. She was a business woman, then in her late 50s with black straight hair, and quite attractive in a strange sort of way. I knew she had visited many parts of Spain and had accidentally come across Denia by train. It was the lemon train, used for travel from Alicante to Denia through the citrus groves and around the edge of the mountains. Scary? I felt if this place was good enough for Madge, it would be good enough for us.

So the following month Michael returned to Denia, this time I accompanied him it being the weekend of our birthdays. The kids were shared between my mum and

Michael's. We arrived with the rain, as February is normally a wet month in Spain but a good time to view and buy a property. Let's face it: if a place looks good in the winter months, especially in the rain, it's going to look even better in the summer. We were looking for an apartment in the 90,000 Euro bracket but Ron had other ideas. He picked us up at Alicante airport. I hadn't flown for a few years and after having Sarina, my confidence was still 'postnatal', not good. So a couple of vodkas during the flight went down a treat. I looked forward to meeting Ron. The lads had talked so much about him, as well as their visit to this part of Spain. The drive to Denia was very interesting and it was just as Michael had described: desert land to begin with until we passed Benidorm, a place I hadn't seen in years, set in complete cloud and threatened by rain. My God, it had grown to a place full of high-rise hotels and apartments, occupied by British holidaymakers, I guess. A place I would have to visit. 'Who's Sticky Vicky?' I asked seeing her name graffitied on a stone wall.

'She does a special sex act in Benidorm, she removes objects from her.' Ron stuttered, and then Michael picked up the answer.

'Jo, she's a kind of an illusionist, she pulls flags and ping pong balls from her moo, moo.'

'You're joking me?' I was shocked. 'How do you know that Michael?'

'Jo, she's been around for years, she's infamous.'

Then Ron stepped in with 'Oh, she's retired now, her daughter does the act.' *Nice,* I thought, *talk about keeping it in the family.* Ron then gave me the low down on Benidorm, so I wasn't in too much of a rush to visit. I tried to view both sides of the road but there was so much to take in, lots of open space, quite green, not too 'deserty'. There were the surrounding mountains with properties on them taking advantage of the views, with some uncompleted apartments, too. I wondered how transport reached these high locations; and felt vertigo just by looking up. There were open spaces towards my right revealing far below the crystal blue sea but the altitude gave me a nervous headache as soon as I realised how high up we were at this point. Ahead was the mountain tunnel; the car went into complete darkness for a split second until Ron switched on his head lights, and then explained the history of the tunnel: how much dynamite it had taken to explode the entrance, so that a new road, the AP7, could be built through. As we came out of the tunnel, rocky rugged mountains appeared on either side with several large sized properties built on them. We had now left the glistening sea behind us. The land ahead became greener, with a richer beauty of citrus, olive, and almond trees and various wild flowers. How lush it all looked. We soon reached the tolls and then followed the main road to Denia, passing large shop units that looked expensive after which a nicely decorated building attracted my attention. On It there were sketches of people walking towards a light.

'Ron, what's that building over there?' I asked pointing towards it.

'The crematorium,' Ron explained, and then went into a long explanation on death. Michael tried to make a joke 'I bet people are dying to get in there.' Sadly, the joke was lost in foreign translation. Ron didn't understand the humour and carried on with his knowledge of death in Spain: 'Most Spanish aren't cremated; normally they're buried within 24-48 hours.'

'That's quick,' Michael replied, 'what about cremation?'

'The same, 24 hours, 48.'

'Why so quick?' He asked.

'The bodies decompose in the heat. Burials are taken to a recess, a stone built structure which they rent for a vast amount of years, then they're moved to a burial ground.' So we then knew all about death in Spain, notwithstanding I was keener to know more about life here.

Ron once again took us straight to Marques de Campo, as he had on Michael's trip. It didn't look quite its best in heavy rain. Michael felt disappointed by this, as he wanted me to see this street as he had, in brilliant sunshine. But I could see beyond the rain, and straight away I was intrigued by the history of this street and Ron was sufficiently knowledgeable to give me all the information I required.

'What are these trees Ron? That overhang the road.' They were leafless and resembled a skeletal structure, large and branchy, inhabiting the length of the Marques de Campo.

'They're plane trees, and they've been here since before the Civil War, at the time of the dry raisin industry, which back then supplied the Co Op with raisins. The English ladies had insisted that the mayor, plant the trees so as to shield them from the sun, and to beautify the street. They blossom during the summer.' Which I hoped they did, they looked rather nude at the moment.

The banks and notaries are also found along this thoroughfare where many business deals are conducted. From the main street, branch lots of side roads consisting of many more shops, offices, bars and restaurants. The end of Marques de Campo takes you to the infamous castle, now a ruin but still very popular with the tourists. Ron explained, 'Denia Castle was built in the 11th and 12th century and offers magnificent views of the sea, city and countryside. There is also a museum attached to the castle, with plenty of intriguing history.'

I was enjoying the history lesson, this was something that came with age and I respected my surroundings. Also I was excited about being here with the prospect of a holiday home to buy. Ron intrigued me, with his dark specs and swished back black hair, rather handsome but far too skinny for my liking. At first I was quite hostile towards him; I felt he was here to rip us off, as some estate agents did back then. Michael reminded me he was different and honest; I understood he was here to do his job, which I eventually respected.

We sat and had drinks on the Marques de Campo in a rustic bar, quite modern but cold, while we discussed properties. Ron informed me of the local area, 'They close this road on Sundays for the cyclists and pedestrians. Denia's very popular with cyclists, which is why there are cycle paths all around. National Spanish and European cycling teams come here to train, especially on the steep roads, like the Montgo, the elephant mountain that divides Denia and Javea.' I instantly liked the Marques de Campo.

'Are all the shops closed, because it's Sunday?' I interrupted, not really listening to Ron's conversation being interested in shopping, like most females.

'Yes, they're all shut, except the one over the road; it only sells newspapers, groceries and milk.'

'Not like England then, the shops are open 7 days a week, and some, like the supermarkets, are 24 hour,' I explained.

'Spain is still very traditional; here all the shops close every day for siesta, at around one thirty, two till five. Sundays all day.' *Let's hope I don't forget that,* I thought. The rain got heavier but after several more drinks we took our chances with the weather and left to view our first property.

It was a two-bed terrace, not to my liking, too small

and the staircase dangerously steep without banisters; it was located behind a senior school, situated just in front of the Montgo, the elephant mountain. The next property we looked at was one Michael liked, out of our price range, but that was Michael and me all over.

Madge and her partner, 'The Lodger', now joined us. We were pleased to see them, I respected Madge's opinion, but 'The Lodger', could keep his. Sid owned a very old two-bed apartment along the Las Marinas road, the beach road that left Denia; we were staying with them that weekend. Now retired, tall and slightly overweight, his hair was white. Both he and Madge had now been in Spain eight months, learning, that is trying to learn the language as best as they could by taking an intense course in Spanish.

Theirs was a strange relationship. They met whilst still married to their partners, sex was the main attraction, and once they were found out, inevitably they were thrown together. A bit harsh. To start with Sid became 'The Lodger', with extras. When they both lived in England he lived in Madge's property and paid rent with a rent book. Their roles were reversed in Spain now, Madge living in Sid's property and putting money into a kitty, which was amicable.

The rain chucked it down. I was wearing only a light jacket having thought I'd go to Spain for some sun. We now approached a street with small palm trees on both sides. There were two-and three-bed bungalows, all matching in yellow and white, newly built. This small desolate urbanisation, Deveses Playa, was about to become a large construction site for many more properties, villas and apartments with some additional shops, restaurants and a gymnasium. Not that we were aware of this plan at the time. There were only three streets for us to view and one show home, as the property available to us to buy was not yet built. So we would have to buy off-plan that can be very risky. Builders have been known to go bust with people's deposits or simply disappear as quickly as they appeared. Or building permission may not have been granted and as a result, purchased properties are demolished by the authorities just after cash completion. Or the Spanish government may decide to build a road or motorway through someone's grounds. Very little compensation is received, if any at all.

We were dealing with a large construction company and that made us feel at ease. We could see for ourselves that the company was an established one. When we arrived at the show home, my first impression was that it was small, but I was desperate to buy. We liked the property mainly because it was new. Walking in through the front door was the lounge. Adjoining this was a small American kitchen; to the left, on either side, were the two bedrooms, separated by a bathroom. From the kitchen was the back door and a small outside terrace which led to stairs up to a double room with an en-suite and a large terrace overlooking Pego. Beneath these stairs, an iron gate led to the communal swimming pool, which backed onto the would-be neighbour's property. In torrential rain we were then taken to the plot where our house would be built. The plot was a muddy wasteland, not suitable for the stilettos I had on, and so I stepped around the puddles and held on to Michael.

'So Ron, the land in front of the property, what is that going to be?'

'Green belt,' he explained.

Bullshit I thought. 'What are those electric boxes, then?' He dismissed this question and just hurried me out of the pouring rain, back into his car and soon forgot the question I had asked. It had been a long wet day, and confusion swept my mind; we had only seen a couple of properties that were the only ones Ron had on his books.

We returned back to Sid's apartment and discussed our options with a couple of glasses of wine, sitting out on their aged terrace which was full of unmatched clutter, colourful pots of all shapes and sizes, and cat litter trays for the four housebound cats and a rather large satellite dish.

'Jo, look, don't rush into this, there are loads of properties for sale here in Denia, look in the newspaper.' Madge handed me the *Costa Blanca News*, a large thick newspaper. It was a local English paper full of expat information and advertisements. I had looked through it that morning and yes there were pages of property for sale on the Costa Blanca, but I was scared.

'I know Madge, but what if we get ripped off? Ron has a reputable company and I trust him. Kind of, well he has come highly recommended from a professional company Michael has researched.' I had heard so many stories of Brits losing their money to con artists, I just didn't want to be one of them. This was all foreign to us and we were looking at a lot of money. 'I'm sure we can get a cheaper property, but we've run out of time, it's our last day tomorrow and we can't keep flying to Spain.'

'I understand, well it's your decision at the end of the day. Do you want another glass of wine? Michael; another beer?' Madge asked.

'Yeah, why not.' I answered. Michael was in deep conversation with Sid, discussing satellite dishes and English telly, how it is broadcast to Spain. He acknowledged Madge with a nod to her question. Then handed her an empty glass.

'So do you fancy Denia market tomorrow morning?' She asked.

'Definitely, let's hope it's sunny,' I muttered, with a mouthful of wine. We finished that afternoon and evening drinking and snacking on Spanish Tapas, talking rubbish as the night drew in.

Madge had us up extra early the next day for the market. Michael wasn't so keen, preferring to stay in bed. But as Sid was going, so was Michael. The weekend had flown by very quickly. We had sunshine that morning, what a difference: everything looked so much better, especially the clear blue sky. It was market day in Denia and everyone was out; after a weekend of rain, there were more people about than we had seen until now. While we walked around the different stalls, we could hear the panpipes playing. Michael wandered off to watch. *'Cuanto cuesta?'* Madge kept asking the stallholders.

'What does that mean?' I asked.

'How much is it?' So that's exactly what I began to ask. The only problem was, when they told me the cost, I couldn't understand their answer. I knew from that point I needed to learn the language. Madge helped me out as best as she could with the language when I made my purchases that morning. It was a large market that sold just about everything: clothes, shoes, fruit, veg, sweets and everything else you would expect to see at a market. Aisle upon aisle, there must have been about ten, not that I counted, and Madge made sure that we walked up and down every one of them. At last Madge suggested 'Shall we go find the men and get a drink?' this was music to my ears; I thought she'd never ask, so off we went. Naturally, the guys were already sitting outside a Spanish café sipping beer in the sunshine. Now I was in heaven: sunshine and a large Vodka and Coke. What more could an Essex girl ask for! I took my sweater off to reveal a vest top underneath, rolled my joggers up to my knees and relaxed with my eyes closed, face up to the sun. I hoped to catch a little tan that day. Our minds were set by the end of the weekend. Signed and sealed on what we had viewed, our decision was made. It would be the *Deveses Playa* property.

Never buy off-plan, as we did. The payment structure is not an entirely safe or secure method. We paid 3,000 euros up front as a deposit but I felt quite nervous at this stage as we hadn't yet sold our house in England with another payment due soon. The first 30 per cent of the total property value was due to secure a start on construction. Conveniently we had now sold at this stage and went into rented accommodation. Within a year a further 30 per cent payment was required to ensure the roof would go on, with the final balance to be paid upon completion. So there's no chance to change one's mind, or to request the property be finalised sooner than scheduled. Unfortunately, the builder is normally in control and in our case he was. One to one and a half years was our expected completion date, so a six- month delay wasn't too much stress. I'd heard worse.

* * Completion of our Spanish home * *

Both Michael and I had flown out to Spain in the January of 2005 to sign the papers at a notary, which finalised completion. The excitement mounted as our dream home was now ready to inspect. We were handed a 'snag' list by the builder together with a large set of keys and piles of paperwork that we had to sign. The Spanish do love their paperwork, for this reason we invested in a filing cabinet. Without your paperwork, there will be problems and that's when the Spanish shoulder shrug is most prevalent. We arrived at the house at the same time as our electrician, it was good timing, especially as we had no light fittings! This was normal for all new builds. Electricity, yes we had, which at the time was signed over to us from the builder with more paper work and the same with the water contracts. We had chosen our light fitments and furniture a few months back, during a quick visit. A few days prior to exchange of contracts we purchased our cutlery, crockery, bed linen and towels at a good price from a Chinese bazaar in Denia. The Chinese have the monopoly on household goods, renowned as the cheapest but not necessarily the best, but good enough. So 30 snags later, our list was completed, and I was worn out.

'Come on, let's go for a walk and see what's around?' I suggested.

The green-belt land opposite was no longer the so-called green belt as described to us when we first viewed the area. Both Michael and I looked around as we walked. So much had changed. The electric boxes I questioned Ron about on that dreadful day of rain belonged to a large number of apartments that were already up and half built. The surrounding area was now a building site, dust and dirt flicked up all over the place. This didn't worry me; all I was concerned about was our house. We walked a further five more minutes, which took us to the N332, the coast road to Alicante and Valencia. At first I was troubled by the lack of noise of traffic on such a busy road. It was quiet due to the larger motorway, the AP7, having been recently built alongside the N332. The AP7 now held the large volume of traffic, it being bigger and better. But it was costly because of the toll booths. Now standing on the edge of the N332, we both took in what was around us, which wasn't a lot. Opposite were large industrial units and shops. There were no cafés or bars to be seen; I felt a little disappointed. There was nowhere to eat or have a drink, and it was very rural. Then I spotted some red lights flickering in the distance as the evening drew in.

'Look, Michael, we live near a nightclub.' Large red

letters flashed *Night Club*. Michael was hesitant in his reply. Should he tell me or not?

'Sorry Jo, but out here in Spain, Nightclubs aren't Nightclubs. They're whore houses.'

'No, you're joking. You mean to tell me, we live near a whore house?'

'Oh come on, its miles away, at least 25 minutes walk.' No he didn't quite understand where I was coming from. I left the conversation there. *How did he know it was only 25 minutes walk away? Stop it* I told myself, *I should trust him.* We returned back to the house with my thoughts still on a whore house nearby disturbing me. Only then did we discover more disturbing news, which was that neither of us had a set of keys. I thought Michael had picked them up and he thought I had. We both had no keys to our new home. *How embarrassing.*

'Ok, let's go and introduce ourselves to our new neighbours.' Michael suggested. Our neighbours had already moved in three months ago and they kindly helped us to get back in to the house; luckily they were both English. Or so I thought at the time. We had pressed their buzzer and waited patiently for someone to come. A woman with lots of hair, curly and wild, came to her gate to greet us.

'Hello, what can I do for you?' She asked. We explained our situation. Sandra was Spanish, but had been brought up in England, by her parents who had been evacuated there during the Civil War. Having only spoken Spanish with her parents at home, and English the rest of the time, she took on all our English traits. However, growing up in England and having a family of her own and then losing both her parents, she no longer spoke Spanish until she returned to her home country to retire with her English husband, Toni. She spoke only her childhood Spanish, but could not write it. Toni was a tall, slim, white-haired English gentleman. He seemed very quiet compared to his wife, or maybe he couldn't get a word in. Sandra was a chatterbox. After a couple of hours listening to Sandra's life story, we eventually succeeded into breaking into our new home

Our long-term plan was now in motion. We returned to England excited with the thought of one day living permanently in our new home in Spain.

* * *Café bar owners* * *

First day in Andrew's bar: we had marigolds, bleach, a skip and decorators. Wilson, our South American builder who still hadn't finished our patio, was under clear instructions. 'The bar needs to be completed within three days and two nights, ready to open.' I soon learnt to understand the phrase *manana, manana,* especially with builders. They would take a deposit to start the job then leave it to start another job repeating the same exercise. Rather than turn any work away, they would run up to four different jobs at any given time. Needless to say, once a deposit was paid, the job was *fucgotten* resulting in a very long wait for completion.

Our money was being spent left right and centre to give this bar a facelift, and that's exactly what it got. We employed Jenny, a girl whose mum had just sold an English bar only two kilometres away, so I saw her as a valuable asset. She taught Michael and me how to cook an English breakfast as well as other snack food in less than five minutes. She also advised us on how to run the business, such as the tab system in Spain. Customers don't pay until they are ready to leave (similar to a restaurant, where you eat and drink and pay at the end). What a great system. Well, like most things here in Spain, there are some flaws. For example, some people got drunk and on occasion they would forget to pay their bill, accidently of course. Some took advantage of this system and so we had to keep our wits about us. Sometimes a patron would be presented with the wrong bill, which often happened, especially when we had live music or during a football Premiership match on T.V and the bar was packed. After a while, everyone starts to look the same. Other times when taking over from someone's shift during a particularly crowded and busy time, they would have written down on their tab, 'The man with the red baseball cap' and he then takes it off! Mind you, there were the funny ones that staff would describe as 'The lady with the big knockers.' (Michael would always be guilty of writing that as he is a boob's man) or 'The man with the big buck teeth' so when they would come to pay you couldn't help staring even harder at their features, 'That will be twenty teeth, please.'

We had to be firm with this tab system as we soon realised there were dodgy characters such as Glasgow Gary, the local druggy, thief, conman who would run up a large tab, then leave, owing money never to be paid. They mainly targeted English bars, so these characters were never allowed a tab; they had to pay as they went. Because we had Jenny working for us, it gave us a head start on these villains. She was four years younger than me: 31, slim, wore her dark hair off her face for work that suited her and she was popular with the punters. She had lived in Spain for three years and had worked for her mum and mum's boyfriend in their bar, until the boyfriend got the boot. The boyfriend was a bit of a Jack, not the lad, like he seemed to think of himself. He followed the organ between his legs, as some men do. Yes, he'd parked it in the wrong place and eventually got caught. Having got the boot, he took over the bar leaving Jenny out of work.

Anyway, our opening night was OK but it could have been better. Sarina played up Grandma and Grandma played up us, so I didn't feel too comfortable leaving them together at home that evening. But I had no choice. This upset was happening prior to my mum's arrival, which worried me; I wanted my mum's visit to be a happy one and I didn't want anyone spoiling that for us.

I stood back behind the bar that evening and watched Michael and Jenny serve the customers, and then I served one or two. My first one just happened to be Glasgow Gary. I soon learnt what a Glasgow smile was that night as Gary had one on his face: a scar slit from the corner of his mouth about two inches long, I'd never seen one before. To begin with I took his banter as I had little option. 'So it's free drinks tonight?' He soon got his reply, and not the one he wanted. 'Is this your first night?' He asked, whilst nudging his mate with a grin, and then both of them looked towards me as if I was stupid. 'I'll have a *caña*, as they're not free.' I walked over to the beer pump, ignoring his comments. *Please god let me pour this idiot's beer.* I could feel his eyes on me, he was waiting for me to make a mess, and I didn't disappoint him. I pulled down the beer tap, tilting the glass whilst the beer poured. Suddenly, splat, splutter, the barrel had finished and as a result the tap spat back at me, straight into my face, froth spurted everywhere. Michael rushed over to my rescue; he pushed the beer tap back to stop it, pushing me out of the way at the same time.

'It's alright, the barrels finished,' he exclaimed, then looked at me and laughed. So did my new admirer, Glasgow Gary. I felt humiliation and heat all at the same time.

'You'll have to wait for Michael to change the barrel.' I glared at him and walked out into the kitchen to dry myself and pick up what was left of my self respect. Jenny rushed after me, 'Are you ok?'

'I'm fine; I'm just drying myself off, honestly.' I smiled and tried to laugh off the whole experience. I knew Jenny felt for me at the time as she hesitantly returned back to the bar. I could hear Glasgow Gary laughing and joking on my account; I felt quite intimidated by this guy and instantly disliked him. I realised then, that the evening was going to be a long one, especially after my beer tap experience. I decided to sit the other side of the bar and let Jenny do the serving. *I could learn the bar duties another night,* I told myself.

Michael gave me vodka; I think he could see the upset on my face when I had left the kitchen. Glasgow Gary was chatting to someone outside, I purposely stayed well away.

That same night I also learnt about the Eastern Bloc. I was warned by several of the punters, 'stay away, most of them are gypsies and will rob you blind; they're dangerous and not to be trusted.' Naturally, this scared the hell out of me. *What had we got ourselves into?* Buying a bar was more dangerous than I'd imagined. We had two guys in from Romania, both young, tall, fit and muscular. At first I thought these guys were here for money, a protection racket possibly? No, they just wanted a drink. Michael charged them as they went and no tab was given them. Thankfully, Andrew had arrived by now. I relaxed and felt safer in his presence. *God, this is different from life in Essex: my safe haven of a hairdressing salon, doing the same client's hair day in and day out with the same routine. But if this is the price to pay, so be it.* My life was about to change dramatically; no time to brood on postnatal depression or how vulnerable I had become since having Sarina. Weakened mentally from childbirth, Mother Nature had left her mark on me. I had become very sensitive, small fears were blown into large problems and with the occasional panic attack, there was far too much nervous energy and never enough oxygen. So it was time to get tough and return to the woman I once was. The Woman of Substance!

My mum was our next visitor. I was concerned about mixing Mum and mother in-law, but they were fine. I think my own mum could sense the tension that had developed over the past two weeks, and she made a special effort to smooth things out. Also, I think April wanted to ease the atmosphere. My mother, in her late 50s, slim, fit and very modern, flew out alone which I knew was very nerve-racking for her. But I sensed the relief that she had shown Michael when he had picked her up from Alicante airport, an hour's drive away. I started to feel a bit more settled with my mum near to discuss my concerns. Mum and I relaxed by the pool most of that week and we concentrated on our tans. Sarina swam with her armbands and an assortment of inflatables, whilst April would read the daily paper in between doing her word search puzzle. Our swimming pool was fifteen metres by six; not massive but comfortably shared with our neighbours, a mix of English, Spanish and one odd German whom, may I say, was rather odd but likeable. Like all communal swimming pools, it came with a list of rules that I naturally broke in the first year of living there. The rules went a bit like this: no ball games, no food or drink, no inflatables, no diving, no sun chairs and the pool was not to be used during siesta times, between three and five o'clock in the afternoon. Oh, and no dogs although I must say there were a few around but say no more. This was all displayed on a sign by the pool and was enforced by the president, Sergeant Sandra who naturally fell into the role and who also happened to be our next-door neighbour. When not relaxing by the pool or breaking the rules, we took a tour of the local bars and restaurants as I did with my father and Donna's visit.

I think at the time, my mum was impressed with my driving skills in a foreign country. Little did she realise I had my boundaries and kept to non-busy roads. So off we went one day to the *Parrot Bar* for lunch. also based along the Las Marinas road, only two minutes' drive from our bar. This is a wide road with a cycling path beside it, which runs flush with the beach, ten minutes from where we lived. April also decided to join us, which was worrying.

This restaurant bar was owned by a Dutchman who offered a large selection in food: Spanish, Dutch, German, French and English. The restaurant was ideally situated on the edge of a sandy beach in Denia that stretches for approx. 15 kilometres, and leads to an adjoining 20 kilometres of coastline. At this time of year the glistening blue Mediterranean Sea is occupied with windsurfers, pedlars and kayaks. On a clear blue day one can view all the way up to Valencia from this restaurant. Sadly that day it was a little hazy, so the view of Valencia wasn't so clear. The beaches were packed with sun worshippers; although a lot of the Spanish were now leaving with their sun brollies and beach bags to enjoy their lunch and afternoon siesta.

An added bonus for our daughter's and the other guests entertainment, was feeding the overfed parrots for the cost of 20 cents. Not to mention the small wishing pond where wishes evaporate with the odd coin and in which I happen to have a good investment, non-returnable of course and no different to the average bank. April was quite taken with the wishing pond; she offered Sarina an assortment of coins, whilst mum and I took our seats on the terrace overlooking the sandy beach and all its occupants. I wanted to show off this part of Denia to the mums, so they could understand why we had come here to live: for the sun, sea and sand.

'So, where did you say Valencia was?' my mother asked, looking in the wrong direction.

'To the left mum.' she stood up, and vaguely saw an outline of the coast leading to Valencia. There was something to be said for having your eyes lasered, she saw better than me.

'Mummy, can I have more money for parrots.' Sarina had returned and broken our peace.

'One sec, babe.' I reached into my mummy bag and fetched Sarina 20 cents to feed the parrots. I gave her two coins which guaranteed at least another ten minutes of quality time with my mum. Her other grandma was waiting over at the parrot enclosure; she actually looked like she was enjoying herself and had come out of the strop she had been in for two weeks. The parrot enclosure was open with a brick wall surrounding it.

They were secured by their ankles with a small link chain and were perched on an old tree that had been cut down and designed for their occupancy. Empty sunflower shells were found everywhere, mainly on the floor. But they still ate what was thrown at them, especially when handed to them by the odd brave individual.

This helped me to relax and enjoy our afternoon; even so I just dreaded what April was going to order for lunch. 'Salad.' *Thank you God, no restaurant could go wrong with a salad.* Until I asked,

'What do you want with your salad?' *Shit, now I've done it,* 'Chicken,'

'No,' she replied abruptly.

'Tuna,' shit, *I'd forgot about her not liking Chicken, here we go again, another magical merry go round.*

'No,'

'Cheese,' my mother interrupted. Silence, 'they have cheese April, its here on the menu.'

'Yes I'll have cheese.' Saved by my mother, jackpot, yes, she loved cheese, and my Mum reminded her of this. There were no questions asked about what kind of cheese as neither of us gave her that option. Mum and I had chicken, Sarina just had chips and shared our chicken. I had taken the bucket and spade so once Sarina had eaten, she would then play next to us on the beach.

'Mum, another glass of wine, April, lemonade?' I asked whilst the waitress was standing there in front of us. Not a very attractive waitress, quite ugly, with rotten teeth, but very pleasant, from Romania. I soon became familiar with the eastern bloc people. They were popularly employed here in Spain, cheap labour.

'Yes please.' They both answered.

'So is that a blue flag I see?'

'Yes Mum every year Denia is awarded a blue flag for its clean beach; that was another factor that attracted me to this area. Ron brought us to this restaurant when we first visited Denia. He and his family once owned it and I remember him telling me about the beaches here, and how you could see Valencia on a good day.' Suddenly I noticed the 'looky, looky' man approach us, as did Sarina so she stopped playing with her bucket and spade almost immediately to see his wares. The 'looky, looky' men here in this part of Spain either come from Africa or Morocco, selling handbags, watches, sunglasses, rugs or tablecloths and occasionally fake designer t-shirts. Sarina soon became familiar with the bartering system; naturally she had a good teacher.

'Not another bag.' April remarked sarcastically while mum, Sarina and I searched through the leather handbags that hung over the 'looky, looky' man's shoulder. He now plonked the whole selection on to our table.

'Yes April, my Mum's looking for a bag for work.' I retorted. Thinking, *stick that in your tea and stir it.* Naturally this shut her up. She thought I was adding to my own collection of handbags.

'cuanto vale?'. (How much) I asked,

'Seisenta euros.' (sixty euros) Does he think I'm British? He needs to think again - I'm Essex. Mum paid 15 euros for her bag that day; Sarina left with a watch; as for me, yes I managed to persuade myself to have another handbag, much to April's disapproval.

The afternoon was a pleasant one, very relaxing and enjoyed by all, even April.

The next day I took Mum and Sarina to the elegant boutiques and perfume shops of Denia; mum was surprised by their costly prices. I needed to pay an electric bill for the bar as the direct debit hadn't been set up in time to pay that first month so Andrew gave us the bill and said to go to any of the banks listed on the statement, which I did. We found the nearest bank and queued for ten minutes then I realised everyone had a ticket, 'Mum, look, everyone's got a ticket, can you see the machine?'

'Yes it's over there; I'll stay here while you fetch one.' The machine was similar to what you might find in a delicatessen. So over I walked nervously thinking, *shit I hope I understand how to retrieve the damn ticket,* especially as it was surrounded by onlookers. Mission accomplished, there was hope for my Spanish, although to be fair the machine had only one red button to press. I returned back to the queue now with my ticket, huffing and puffing at mum. We waited twenty minutes or more until eventually we reached the desk. Incredibly there were only two cashiers available with about 20 to 30 waiting customers. I handed the bill and the correct cash to the cashier. He looked at it and then shook his head no, and pointed to the notice beside him. I stood back for ages to translate in my head what it said, then realised that the bank didn't accept utility bills after 10.30am. I glanced at my watch, it was 10.38; I was eight minutes too late. I looked at the man behind his desk, offering him a pleading look. He shrugged his shoulders up, held them for a split second, then released them, and looked over my shoulder for his next victim, dismissing me altogether. 'Can you believe that mum, a bank refusing payment of a bill?' Before I left I had to re-read the notice, just to check I hadn't misunderstood, still in disbelief. I returned back to the notice, looking around myself to check who was watching me. I felt slightly embarrassed whilst I approached the desk, I'm sure the clerk who had refused my payment was thinking; *dumb English girl trying to pay her bills at the wrong time.* I didn't look at him; my eyes were focussed only on the sign that was beside him. I then noticed that not only was there a certain time of day one had to pay bills in that particular bank, but it also stated in Spanish, that there were certain days of the month. So I had to wait another two weeks to pay the electric bill. How crazy was that? But it's not money for them. We then left to enjoy lunch on the Campo and soak up the Spanish atmosphere. I was still frustrated by the bank incident but a couple of glasses of wine washed my frustration away.

My mum's departure soon came round; we'd enjoyed our time together. April decided to return to England with her, which was for the best for her to return back to her familiar surroundings and routine, and for me to live my dream.

* * *Kindergarten and beggar* * *

I was recollecting the series *The High Chaparal*. It was a western about a ranch with cattle. This setting was very similar to Sarina's new nursery without the cattle, only herds of children. It was based between Denia and Els Poblets on the back road, if one blinked one would miss it driving by. It is a house set in large grounds with palm trees; to reach it, we had to drive up a short shingle path with only, enough room for one car. This was the only access to the nursery; and there were no other properties built there. We then found a small car park at the end that belonged to the guarderia (day nursery), a very large finca [country house] that had been renovated with a high-bricked wall surrounding it, as well as a solid wooden gate. I was nervous as we approached the property, 'Michael, we should have brought someone with us to translate.'

'Oh, we'll be ok; we can always come back with a translator.' This was true I thought. We banged hard on the gate for someone's attention. After several loud knocks and a few repeated *'Holas,'* a young girl answered, *'Digame,'* (Tell me).

'Habla Ingles?' (You speak English)? I asked.

'No.' she answered. *Great, how do I explain this?* I thought. Then by some miracle a woman was passing through the gate to collect her daughter and overheard the conversation.

'I speak English, can I help?'

'Yes please, would you mind?' Relief swept over me. I had only studied a little Spanish at college, passing level 1. So now I realised that I needed to learn to speak more Spanish if I was to live here. The young girl invited us through the gate, 'Hola,' she said to Sarina, poking her finger under Sarina's armpit to tickle her. Sarina was in her Daddy's arms burying her head into his chest, acting shy.

'Say hello, Sarina.' Sarina just ignored my request; *kids always know how to let you down,* I thought. We entered the garden; it was enormous with traditional hardy Spanish grass, the stuff that pricks you as you sit on it. We were shown through the large gazebo area that led to the wooden *naya* (conservatory) area, and then into the house to where the office was. As we passed through the nursery I couldn't help noticing their large pine wood kitchen, it was spotlessly clean and tidy; *obviously they cook on site,* I thought.

Now comfortably seated in her office, the young girl introduced herself as Paula, pronounced as Baula. She was French and spoke Spanish fluently; a slim pretty girl, she ran the business with her mother. We began with asking the usual questions: opening times, prices, activities and whether the food was included. We questioned the prices, 'how much for the month?' I asked the mum translator,

'168 euros.' She replied.

'For the month?' I repeated, 'Full time hours, breakfast, lunch and tea?'

'Yes, is that a problem?' The mother asked whilst translating and looking puzzled at Paula.

'No, not at all.' *Shut up Jo* I thought. Then Michael couldn't help himself.

'That's cheap; we used to pay five hundred pounds per month, part-time hours as well in England.' I kicked him just as he finished his sentence. I didn't want Paula knowing this as she may have been tempted to increase our fees, especially as we were British. I think the mum translator realised that, especially when Michael yelped as I kicked him. The conversation ended there. I felt quite comfortable with Paula and her fees; I think at the time Spain subsidised the costs to help working families.

'Ok, I must leave now.' Up stood our translator.

'Thank you so much.' Both Michael and I stood to shake her hand. Now quite satisfied with our answers, we organised a start date and then left.

On the First day of nursery I stayed with Sarina for the first two hours. I was scared to leave her straight away, especially as she didn't speak their language. So I felt this was going to help her to settle in, and naturally, as a mother, I felt protective. Of course, this was a disaster, an eye opener and a complete nightmare. The carers, all two of them, once they realised I was there to stay for a short while, just stared at me with disbelief, probably thinking, *'Oh she's made a rod for her own back.'* By golly I had. But at the same time, I couldn't believe my eyes. I watched the children arrive, one or two at a time. There must have been 20 or more toddlers if not more, all shapes and sizes, between one to two years of age. I love kids, but when they come in numbers, I become 'neurotic' when in their company. I watched them run, scream, cry and play wild in this large garden with climbing frames, toys, swings scattered every-where. No discipline, only cattle, mayhem, unorganised at that, or was that my British mentality? I was used to five children to a carer, supervised within a small classroom. Well, these kids were everywhere. This was too much, Sarina was terrified, she stayed strapped to my lap for a whole 2 hours, and I knew then that I wasn't going to leave without a tantrum. I stood up and took her over to the climbing frame where another little girl was playing, but she left once she took one look at us, outsiders. 'Come on Sarina, come and play here.' I encouraged, then glanced around and had another shock. The third carer had arrived. *Man, a man, would you believe it?* A man who looked after children. I had to blink twice. He was a thin, dark-haired guy in his thirties.

'Hola, soy Eduardo.' (Hello I am Eduardo) he

introduced himself to me and Sarina. My face must have been a picture, he started speaking Spanish and I didn't understand any of it, I just agreed.

'Vale.' (ok). I answered. He could have said anything to me, such as; 'what the hell are you doing staying with your daughter on her first day of nursery you silly bitch.' There was I grinning and agreeing like a dumb blonde. He walked away to greet his herd. He cuddled them, kissed them and then chased them away as he walked over to the *naya* area. I thought I'd stay a little longer as I was now feeling even more uncomfortable about the situation. I had now convinced myself: I was going to stay for the morning, purely for the experience of a Spanish nursery without a thought for the upset I was about to cause Sarina once I left. My attention was then brought back to Eduardo; he had a hosepipe in his hand and was hosing his herd of children. I watched toddlers in their nappies run in all directions, through the gazebo and back again, laughing, giggling. They were having a great time cooling themselves off in the heat. *Truly magical,* a man with his bear cubs. Wasn't this behaviour like it should be, without all the stipulations and rules?. How different this country was compared to England: was this a turning point of my English mentality?

'Sarina, ven conmigo.' (Sarina, come with me). Paula startled my thoughts; yes it was time that I left. I handed Sarina to her, my baby calf screamed, she clung to me with all her might. Paula took her from me and I left not

looking back - I didn't need to see her, I could hear her.

I got into my car and cried pathetically while I drove down the shingle road to the bar for my first morning of work. With a knot in my stomach I felt totally sick having just left my three year old in a foreign nursery with no one who spoke English. I told myself it would get easier tomorrow.

Michael was busy when I arrived at the bar. I tried to share the ordeal that I'd been through but he had other things on his mind. Leaving me to mind the bar alone was one. 'It's only for two hours, who's gonna come in, I just have to go to the wholesalers, you'll be alright.' He grabbed his list and left.

I now felt abandoned, a bit like Sarina. No one to talk to, I was nervous as hell. What if someone does come in for a coffee? Michael hadn't shown me how to use the coffee machine. I put this out of my mind and made a start by cleaning the kitchen just behind the bar. I grabbed some marigold gloves and put them on, trying to think positive. Suddenly I heard the flip and flop of someone's flip flops coming into the bar. My heart began to beat fast. *Shit,* I thought, *a customer!* I came out of the kitchen to the bar area, armed with a mop so I could defend myself if necessary. Well, this is what I told myself when I saw a little, skinny, short-haired man with rotten teeth, a beggar trying to sell me poems. *Great!* Well I ushered him away and said, *'no comprendo.'* He was not amused and still carried on with his pitiful sales pitch in

Spanish. I then had to repeat myself, this time with a more abrupt approach, *'No comprendo.'* He now understood, off he went with his nose up in the air. That was easy enough, I thought, until he reached the top step outside of our bar. He shouted out to me in bold English,

'You're fat' and rushed off, flipping and flopping down my terrace stairs with me and my mop after him.

Call her a bitch, slut, whore but never tell a woman she's fat, especially an Essex girl! OK, I had gained a stone in weight, now weighing in at 10 stone. Was I now fat? What a morning I was having!

Later that day I picked Sarina up from guardaria (kindergarten). I entered the garden area through the large wooden gate, and there sat half the children from the morning session: little angels under two large palm trees eating yoghurt and fruit, much of it on their fingers and faces, but relaxed and more controlled. Sarina was pleased to see me and I her. She had, of course, wet her clothes and was in her spare set. She learnt a new phrase that day: *'pee, pee'* which meant 'Wee, wee.'

It took Sarina three weeks to settle into the *guarderia*. She screamed every morning but I remained focused and positive with the thought that she would be happy when I went to collect her. Well, this was mostly true; sometimes she would be waiting with her rucksack on her back and crying for her mummy to come. The situation wasn't good upsetting me immensely; and it still traumatises me that I had no one to support me during that time. It was upsetting enough for any parent to leave their child on the first day of nursery, but for me it was more difficult: I was leaving my daughter with people who didn't speak her language. How isolated she must have felt. I couldn't speak the language either so I had to rely on my motherly instincts. The guarderia was always clean and the carers always helpful and understanding of the language barrier, and most importantly, I could see that the rest of the children were happy with the set up. On one occasion, Michael took Sarina to the *guarderia*. He did not cope at all. After he had dropped her off screaming, he got into our car and drove around the corner, stopped and wept. He refused to ever take her again. So this job was mine. Being a mum again was becoming hard work - how long was I going to cope with the role before escaping back to full time employment?

Louis was soon to fly out and I was also concerned about him. He was travelling alone. I gave him the normal advice a mother would give to her 16 year old, 'don't accept any parcels, don't talk to anyone and watch your passport and wallet. Oh and don't be late.' Louis was going to spend the summer with us, then return back to England in the September to begin a college course in carpentry. Deep down in my heart I hoped he was going to take an interest in the bar and stay in Spain with his family; after all Louis was my first born and I'd more or less brought him up by myself, so naturally I was feeling the umbilical cord being cut between us again.

* * *The locals* * *

It took several months for the locals to accept us in the bar; some we liked, some we didn't and vice a versa. To begin with, I struggled being alone at home of a night, while Michael worked; often his shift would last till 2am or till 5am most nights. He made lots of friends, some I liked and some I wouldn't offer the saucer to my cup. While I stayed home with Sarina I felt lonely, especially some evenings after putting Sarina to bed. Constantly my mind played tricks on me, I didn't trust Michael, knew I had married a man who had history, having been previously married 3 times, as well as having been engaged to a girl, whom he'd left, because of me. He was A Slut. I'm not a jealous woman nor am I stupid, but there's little worse than having a man cheat on you especially one that you love,

I worked the morning shift with Jenny and Michael worked the evenings with Anne. We were like passing ships never having any time for each other, always one of us having to be at the bar so that it ran smoothly to our specifications and save a wage.

Anne, now she was woman girl in her own right, in

her mid-50's and married to Don who was a little older than herself which she'd pointed out to me on our first introduction, 'This is Don as you can see he is a lot older than myself, so don't think I look good for my age as I am much younger than him'. A marriage matched perfectly within a boxing ring. Why do people stay together? It must be for 'financial feelings' or 'safety security' certainly not SEX.

The morning shift was from 10:00 to 3:00 and consisted mainly of serving breakfasts, and some lunches. Jenny trained me up a treat to cook English breakfast and a selection of readymade lunches. One of us would cook, normally Jenny and the other would be front-of-house to serve and to take food and drink orders; on occasions, as I became more familiar with the job, we would swap roles. I was pretty shit to begin with but Jenny was patient. During the day most of the customers were holidaymakers plus a few residents, one of whom in particular was Denzel. He drank alcohol-free lager by the bottle on a daily basis which was his routine, besides sitting on the beach with his fold up chair treasuring his tan, Until it was time to visit our bar and drive us mad with his difficult personality and his strong opinions, and although he struggled to speak at times, it never stopped him putting his point across. He had suffered throat cancer several years before which had left him requiring a tracheotomy. A white square sticky patch covered his voice box that he held whilst speaking. On occasions he needed to clear the larynx area with his handkerchief, a ghastly and necessary procedure but it never stopped him clearing it in public. He was a man one liked most days but, depending on his mood, one disliked him on other days; but he had a heart. He was now retired and had settled to living his Spanish way of life with his wife Zeta, the sweetest lady one could ever meet.

I began to push my mobile hair dressing which at first was difficult with clients living so far from one another. Not being familiar with the area was quite nerve racking, and I wasn't a confident driver. When some of the local lads did ask how much I charged for a cut, I felt a little nervous because some were piss heads and weren't to be trusted. I was still sussing them out. But where there's a will there's a way, so I'd either cut their hair at my home or I would cut their hair in the bar early before we opened depending on who they were.

Usually I never worked any of the evening shifts, although on occasion I would ask Madge to babysit Sarina - they had a great relationship. This enabled me to help Michael and gave us some time together. Michael wouldn't let me work an evening shift alone.

A lot of the locals visited the bar of an evening, and Michael introduced them to me as and when he could. One particular evening two stocky guys entered the bar; the hairs stood up on my arms as they approached me for a drink, I guess this was my Essex instinct. *'Dos cañas'* the larger one instructed. I stepped to one side and left

Michael to serve them; in fact, anyone I didn't like the look of I refused to serve thus leaving mostly Michael to do the work. Both these guys had their heads shaved, which to me always gave the look of a thug or someone too mean to pay for a haircut. The larger one was called Paul, he had mean-looking eyebrows. They introduced themselves as brothers, not that we were interested. *'Caña,'* he ordered every ten minutes. Paul banged his glass each time on the bar when he wanted a drink, 'Another one please mate.' Why didn't they drink pints, it would have lasted them longer. 'Come on, were living in a hot country, beer gets warm 'ere.' That outburst told me, had he read my thoughts? Although I think in Paul's case, he would have liked to have one run around him, refilling his glass on demand. 'So you're the new owners of Andrew's Bar?'

'Yeah, do you live ere?' Michael asked.

'Yeah, couple of years now. How long you been 'ere?' the larger one asked

'Not long, few months.' Michael answered.

'Few months and you bought this shit ole.' I was now decided: I didn't like this abrupt, rude man. Michael didn't answer this question, he just turned on his heel, picked up a tea towel and began to dry the washed glasses. Paul turned to his brother, smirked towards me and shook out a cigarette from its box, then pointed the box towards his brother implying with a nod did he want one, which he did. The younger brother, Alex, seemed sweeter; he didn't say a lot, not to me any way. Later I found out that Paul was Alex's carer, as he had an abnormality with his brain. He spoke quite slowly and repeated himself a lot, so Paul naturally did all the talking, maybe to disguise his brother's disability. They seemed to know the regulars. One of them, John the gardener, now arrived and took his usual seat at the bar. He had a military routine of three bottles of Heineken, and then always left to go next door to the other English bar, *Cooks,* named after the previous owner. There, he would drink a further four bottles and then leave at 7:45pm precisely to cycle home for his dinner. I observed the locals closely

Sharon then also arrived; she was very familiar with both these two rogues. Michael had already warned me about Sharon as she had been in a few times and had quizzed Michael, after which she concluded her conversation with 'Good luck.' What that meant we didn't know. Had she meant it? Or did we need it?

'Get Sharon a Vodka and Sprite; put it on my bill and dos mas for us.' Paul ordered. Why speak half a sentence in English then switch to Spanish? *I guess they call this Spanglish,* I thought. Paul seemed to me to have a few bob, his bill that evening tallied up to nearly fifty euros. So he was a good client, whether I liked him or not, although I wondered at that time how he earned his money.

Just like Colin, another regular to the bar. He

drank there every day, didn't work, and we only ever saw him in the afternoon, never in the morning. I guess he was in his coffin from four in the morning and arose by three or four in the afternoon. Very mysterious kind of guy - he had no girlfriend, very quiet, kept himself to himself. Apparently he had a bar in Majorca years ago with his ex- girlfriend, had a child, it didn't work out, so the ex moved to England despite being Spanish, and he moved to Denia. He spoke Spanish rather well, handsome kind of guy, thick dark hair, the kind of hair Michael dreams of, no grey. I liked him; he gave me a sense of security whenever he was around.

Sharon- I couldn't quite work her out and I didn't care to; she was a bitch, very cocksure of herself. Michael also disliked her as she had no manners and spoke to us like we were a piece of shit and enjoyed demeaning us in public without caring what she said. I overheard one of her conversations with Paul that night: 'I give um six months.' I took it she was referring to Michael and me. I didn't bother to listen for Paul's answer. What did I care? I knew we were here for the duration, watch this space, babe. Her hair was backdated to the eighties, very similar to Rod Stuart's of the same era. She drank very heavily, took drugs and slept with any guy she could get her claws into, however she was shockingly intelligent with a good job, she managed a hotel. I felt sorry for her staff though, I bet she ran a tight ship, and I believe she did. I couldn't help feeling deep down that all this was a front and that really she was human and that side of her was the side I wanted to get to know.

During the next 6 months, much to Sharon's disappointment, we were still there and we became good friends with the two odd balls, Paul and Alex as well as Paul's girlfriend, Ally, whom he'd not long met. Ally was also new to the country; she and her 17 year-old daughter, Shelley, both came from Essex. They both recently moved in with the brothers, who had a rather large 3-storey property on top of the Montgo, with panoramic views of the castle and the Port. Our first dinner invitation took place here. Paul knew of my phobia of The Montgo and one day he asked me, 'Have you ever been up the mountain?'

'Well of course I have, up and over to Javea and I plan never to go again. I had my head between my knees and Michael couldn't even turn back as the road was so narrow.' A road that ran around the edge of a mountain, joining Denia to Javea; at its highest level you saw the breeze blocks built on the boundary to prevent vehicles from flying over. I assume it would be quite scenic to someone who didn't suffer a phobia for heights.

'I'm having a BBQ next Tuesday. Get Michael to have the night off and come to my house. The Montgo is a very big mountain Jo and you've only seen one small part.' Was this an invitation or an order? Neverthless, I thought it would be nice for me and Michael to have the night off and to make friends.

Paul was right about the mountain, there were different parts and we were visiting the Denia side, although the mountain rises some 753 metres, (2,470 ft) with its rocky formations, cliffs, caves and natural harbours. It is also home to a nature reserve. There are also urbanisations there, mainly populated by villas, built at the bottom of the mountain and reaching half way up in sections from Marquesa 1 to Marquesa 6. It is said a Belgian man bought the mountain many years ago, for the equivalence of £500 and that upon his death it is believed his wife was required to pay taxes of 370000 million in pesetas approx. Well so the gossip goes.

Ally had been an English teacher in the UK, tall and wise, contrary to her daughter Shelley who wasn't and who was only 17 but looked more like 21 years of age. This young woman still had a lot to learn but she was very comical, especially after a few drinks, and could she drink. Ally had met Paul the year before, when on holiday. She had been visiting her long term friend, who lived and worked in Denia; she met Paul in a bar and they shared a holiday romance. They stayed in touch, Paul visiting England a couple of times and the relationship soon blossomed. So Ally made the decision then to move to Spain and work as a teacher.

I was concerned about the journey to Paul's house. How high up on the mountain was he? Not knowing scared me all the more. To prevent us getting lost, Paul met us in La Pedrera, a very small village encased at the bottom part of the Montgo, which consisted of 3 or 4 bars, restaurants and a chemist, very quaint. We met in one of the Spanish bars;, it was busy and full with different nationalities; although very small it had a bar the same length as the room, reaching the glass sliding doors, with only enough room for bar stools.

'Hi Paul, hi Alex.' I greeted the brothers as they entered this tiny little bar.

'What you drinking,' Michael asked as he took his money from his wallet.

'Dos cañas.' The usual, two small beers. I wondered if Paul would bang the bar with his glass here.

'So JJJo, are ya gona lllisten to me play me guitar?' Alex had a small stutter and also had a habit of repeating himself; other than that, to look at him one wouldn't recognise any other disability, he was harmless and quite sweet.

'Yes, Alex, that's what I've come for, especially, oh and to visit this bloody high mountain. I thought you said the mountain resembled the head and trunk of an elephant?' I now looked towards Paul for the answer to my question. He was in deep conversation with Michael and didn't hear my question, although Michael did.

'Yeah, where's the elephant head?' Paul had just gulped his last part of his beer, then answered,

'It's the Javea side, not this side of the mountain.' *Javea*, I thought, *we hadn't properly visited that side yet.*

'Are we having another beer?' a silly question from Michael considering Paul had already ordered another round of drinks.

After 2 glasses of wine, Dutch courage was re-installed so we followed Paul in his car. What a jerk, I still wasn't too sure about him, he drove up the curvy mountain roads like a rally driver, his car wheels screeched on each sharp bend. No, I wasn't impressed; the last 2 bends climbing up were exposed with magnificent views, looking downwards upon various properties. I looked away and held my breath; several houses camouflaged the rest of the views. Finally we parked up. This was along a very narrow un-made road, just outside Paul's property. I chose not to comment about his driving skills, which I thought were those of a delinquent rather than a man in his late 40s.

'This is lovely, Paul. I can't say I had much time to see how high we are, but high enough. It's not at all how I imagined.' The property sloped up the mountain, so there were no sheer drops to overlook.

'I told you, didn't I, come on up.' With that he led us up some steps and into the house that was on separate levels, similar to most on The Montgo. We entered through the front door; this was the main floor where the kitchen, lounge, a couple of bedrooms as well as a toilet were situated. It was soon to be renovated and changed to the lower level. From the lounge were some dodgy stairs with a temporary man-made pole as opposed to wooden banister leading down to a workman's room, full of tools and walls half plastered. This floor also held several un-finished rooms. Another set of steps, this time stone ones, led down to the outside BBQ and swimming pool area. The views were fantastic; I'd never seen such a hair-raising vision, such a picture postcard. Where was my camera? Sarina had run off to make friends, whilst I fumbled for my camera, still wary of my phobia of heights. I stood slightly back from the view and I felt slightly light-headed; *'Where was that wine?'*

We were introduced to another couple, Jane and Cole who were nice, very laid back, and to their daughter, Hayley, who was a similar age to Sarina. We had a lot in common, so naturally we gelled. Cole was responsible for the renovation of Paul's house, which had now become more or less a full-time job more or less. Jane, meanwhile, took care of holiday homes dealing with the change-overs, the cleaning and restoration of the properties in readiness for the next visitor, as well as doing the laundry. This kept her very busy especially during June, July and August, the high season. 'What do you do Jo?' she asked handing me a rather large glass of wine.

'Oh me? Michael and I run a bar in Denia, oh and I'm also a hairdresser.' Had I nearly forgotten I was a hairdresser?

'Oh yeah, Ally said you own Andrew's Bar but never mentioned you were a hairdresser. I'm looking for one, ever since I've lived here, I have been butchered several times by the Spanish, they cannot cut hair. Do you do home visits?'

'Yes, where do you live?'

'Els Poblets.'

'Me too, well near there, we live in El Vergel.' So, I not only gained another new client, I gained a new friend. We hit it off straight away, discussed our children, school and our experiences of being foreign mothers. We also talked about the reason for leaving England to live there. Although I had dreaded the evening, it was one I really enjoyed. The bonus was that now I felt more at ease with The Montgo as well as with Paul.

Another good customer was the car salesman and rightly so, we'd paid him his whack of commission. He came in most nights with his wife, Jan, and his drop-dead gorgeous son, Antony, who was a tad thick, but this was outweighed by his sweetness and charm. His father acted as if he owned the bar, especially on Sunday nights that was our quiz night. His attitude soon changed once I introduced bingo with the quiz and worked on quiz nights myself. I began to regularly work every Sunday, at least until Madge was no longer allowed to babysit; she'd lost her "pass" for the Sunday night and all the other times I needed her. Sid had become obsessive, sadly this ruined our friendship and we no longer kept in touch excepting the odd hello as and when we were passing, which was very rare.

Bingo was a hit on Sunday nights as well as our quiz. It became our busiest night of the week, regulars would arrive early so they could ensure having a table. Anne, our kitchen hand, would reserve her usual table near the dartboard, for her and her friends. There were 5 or more women all at a certain stage of life, thus their quiz team name, 'Post-Menopausal'. The bar comprised of 3 or 4 tables inside but was mainly taken up with a rustic, horse shoe shaped bar with wooden stools which I liked, it enabled people to sit around it and be sociable. Eileen and Bob always held their normal position at the bar, often joined by their neighbours. Ilene was a true Londoner as was Bob, loved Bingo especially when her favourite number, 69, was called.

'Chance would be a fine thing', she would shout, a woman in her sixties, and this would always generate a giggle. She became a legend, the *69 sex-wisher.*

Our outside terrace took 7 tables, and held the sun on it from April to September. Mainly tourists took the outdoor seating, especially if there was still a shimmer of sun. We had a canopy which we often used during the day to protect our clients from the hot sunshine. We had neighbours either side of us, our terraces were joined but separated by a wicker wall one side and a glass enclosure the other. Both neighbours were nice people, Spanish one side and English the other. They were restaurants, so there was no competition.

I was always amazed by the type of people who liked to play Bingo. *Never judge a book by its cover* as I would normally. One Sunday evening when I was working and still trying to decide which customers I liked to serve, I noticed straight away, (it was hard not to), from the corner of my eye, Conner and Patsy. Entering the bar arm in arm, they immediately drew everyone's attention. Now he looked scary, short and stocky, no hair, in fact his head shone with a big tattoo encrypted on the back of his head, CONNER. He also had a rather large bolt with spikes that went through his ear, as an earring. He wore jeans ripped fashionably, but far too tight, with Dr Martin boots; Patsy was 50 years of age, ten possibly fifteen years older than Conner. She dressed as though she was a teenager, exposing a rather large cleavage and her dress was far too tight clinging to her love handles doing her no justice. I watched them order a drink. 'I'll have a pint and a glass of wine,' Conner said. They were already drunk and very loud, I had to walk over and introduce myself.

'Hi, I'm Jo; do you want a Bingo ticket?' *What a question to ask, of course they don't,* I thought, *this couple wouldn't want to play bingo.* I felt myself go red.

'Sure, how much and what do we win?' asked Conner, now slumped against the bar for support.

'Oh, that depends on how many tickets we sell,

normally for a line you can win ten to fifteen euros, full house can be anything from 80 to 100 euros, if not more.' Surprisingly, both their faces lit up and they bought five tickets each; I was shocked. We chatted whilst I tore out their tickets making me feel a little more at ease. Patsy and I ex-changed briefly our life stories, before the bingo started. I liked her; wasn't too sure about Conner, *but that will come* I thought. Patsy was very educated and when sober, spoke several languages; Spanish, Arabic, French and naturally English. Big drinkers and loved Bingo, a colourful couple.

Patsy worked to support Conner's drink habit whilst Conner kept his habit and drank. After their night of bingo Conner then became a permanent fixture within the bar, during the course of the day as well as the night. He would run up bar bills, then settle them and then repeat the whole process once again, he was never in credit and always paid us eventually. As threatening as Conner looked, behind the façade was a guy with past problems, his childhood still torturing him to this day. He also spoke Spanish and he was handy. especially when I was working. I grew to like this Irish man and his pet, Patsy.

Patsy sold investment policies - whether they were legal or not, was another question. She had retired to Spain on her late husband's pension, then worked part time in a bar for pocket money and for something to do, which was where she met Conner. In time, through unforeseen circumstances, she began to live beyond her means. She lost her home and all her assets; this bad fortune brought her and Conner to Denia. *Were they on the run?* She worshipped Conner and he had a spell over her no one could break!

* * Louis, the visitors and the bulls * *

The summer season was now well upon us. Designer Gucci sunglasses, a bottle of after shave, not to mention the designer flip flops and swim shorts he was never to wear, I thought the perfect gift for my son's sixteenth birthday. Michael had left early that morning to collect Louis up from Alicante airport whilst I worked in the bar.

'Morning Conner, the usual? My son comes today, so your get to meet him.' Conner looked up as he strolled in to the bar without his normal bounce, his eyes looked hazy caused from the previous night's drinking. I was sure he was still wearing the same clothes as the day before. Michael had mentioned both Conner and Patsy were in the bar till early hours this morning, pissed out of their heads. James the builder had also been in, entertaining the punters with his magic tricks. This he did most nights at his pleasure. He never charged for his acts, because he said it was a gift he'd learnt at no cost when he was young. An elderly gentleman who had worked the cruise liners had passed a lot of his magic on to James. who at one stage had also belonged to *The Magic Circle*. Unfortunately, his nerves had got the

91

better of him whenever he performed to large audiences, especially in large public areas, so he now only perform-ed in bars where he felt comfortable.

'Yes, the usual, I'll buy him a beer.' Conner broke my thoughts; I'd forgotten what I was doing and raced over to the bar to fetch him his beer.

'He's only sixteen,' Louis wasn't too keen on alcohol anyway.

'Yeah, but didn't you drink at sixteen?' Conner remarked. *Let's not go there* I thought.

'So, Michael says you were in one of James magic tricks?'

'Yeah, how fucking freaky was that? Two birds lifting me and a chair into the air with only two fingers.' I tried to imagine it, but I couldn't; I would need to see this for myself. Apparently James had picked the two smallest, skinniest girls for this trick and yes they did lift him high up into the air, something to do with gravity, levitation I believe. Whilst this was going on Patsy was outside on the terrace exposing her breasts; apparently this was her party trick when she over indulged in wine. I must say she never did this while I was around.

'He can make money float in a beer glass as well.' Michael had also mentioned the beer glass trick, how he made a ten euro note float in a glass and out in to the air in front of him, then he'd slice above and below the note with his hand to show it wasn't attached to anything. I looked forward to meeting this magician.

It had been a busy morning; with English breakfast especially, holiday makers, builders, couple of local expats, as well as some Spanish for their coffees and *canas*. The Spanish always appeared to be in a rush as they would order a drink, light a cigarette, smoke it, drink and leave in less than five minutes, sometimes not even finish what they ordered, leaving a little at the bottom of the glass or cup. Michael had explained that when the Spanish did this, it was a polite gesture, which meant that they would return another time. Conner always conversed with the Spanish clients; his Spanish was good, even with an Irish accent. This helped put me at ease because I could then chat to the English or the customers who spoke English, most of whom did. I was still trying to learn Spanish, which was difficult in an English environment; I had little opportunity to practice the language.

'Lou, Lou,' I ran over to him as he entered the bar. Michael followed behind him. I noticed they both looked tired. I flung my arms around him and hugged him. *Please stay* I thought, *please love it here, don't go back to England,* I wished all this at once.

'Alright Mum, missed you too.' He was embarrassed. Then I noticed a little acne on his face. *Where are his freckles?* I thought. It had only been a couple of months since I'd seen him last, they had obviously disappeared gradually and gone un-noticed over a period of time. *Why had I not noticed?* I was filled with a mother's guilt.

'How was the flight? Were you scared?'

'No mother, I slept. Where's Chucky?' This was Sarina's nickname.

'Oh, she's at *guarderia*, kindergarten, we'll pick her up in a bit. What do you think of the bar?'

'Oh, it's alright'. *Show some enthusiasm* I thought. Louis wasn't keen on our venture, moving to Spain had upset his routine, but he was happy living with my mother, which wasn't too much of an upheaval. Like most nans, she spoilt him. He had spent most of his growing-up years around both my parents, staying with one of them most weekends when I worked or socialised. Both my parents were supportive, when I was a single working mother as were my brother and sister.

'Come on Lou, let's show you around. I'll show you what we've done.' I suggested, leading him around the bar.

We had re-tiled the walls only half way with large pastel blue tiles and painted the remainder wall above a creamy beige colour. We had cleaned, scrubbed and dis-infected. We also painted the bathroom area, and we had changed the toilet seats, put up some fancy shelves and pictures. Our terrace was very small but it had the sun, so we now needed to make the most of it. , We invested in some wicker furniture, very comfortable tables and chairs. This, I felt, would attract the customers, as it always attracted me when on holiday as I would look for the comfy seats first opposed to the menu.

'This is Conner, Conner Louis,'

'Your mum's been telling me all about you.' Louis shook his hand; he looked at Conner strangely. I knew what he was thinking, 'Has his mother taken up with rogues?', and maybe I had.

After a beer, which Conner had insisted on buying, we left to collect Sarina.

Louis was very quiet as we drove down the shingle lane leading to the *guarderia*. I was pleased to have him back. He filled the gap in my heart. But I knew deep down it wasn't to last; I knew he preferred England with his grandparents and friends.

'I haven't told Sarina you're coming so it will be a nice surprise. Have you missed her?'

'Sort off, no only joking, course I've missed her and you and dad.' *Thank god* I thought, *he does still love us all.* I had felt abandoned and wondered if he had felt the same.

'Here we are, wait until we go through those doors Lou, its heaven.' The large wooden doors opened out to the fabulous grounds, to where Sarina now played on a daily basis. Paula was waiting as we entered the garden. I introduced them both in my pigeon Spanish about which at that moment I was very proud.

'Lou, Lou, Lou, Lou,' Sarina screamed as she ran up the garden. Her hair looked a mess, it was fine and whispery, covered in sweat and stuck to her face. Her clothes looked as though she had worn them for a week.

From the way Sarina looked, tired, sweaty with food stains, I was obviously getting my money's worth out of the nursery, because, to me, this was evidence that she had played well and eaten well. Once she reached us, she leapt up and flung her arms around her brother's neck.

'Chucky, have you missed me?'

'It's your birthday tomorrow, I miss you, are you staying forever?'

'We'll see what ya bought me?' Sarina shot me with a questioning look, meaning *what had she bought him?*

'You know what we got him, sssshhh it's a surprise.' By the time we got home Louis and Sarina were already arguing. I stopped the car just in front of our gate, abruptly, so as to interrupt the squabbling pair in the back of the car. Thirteen years difference in age had no affect, Sarina stood her ground as a three year old.

'I haven't got you anything for your birthday, nor has mummy and daddy, kner, knooky, kner, kner.'

Louis then descended to her level, immaturely not acting his age, but hers.

'I bought you a chocolate bar and ate it.' He then poked her in the ribs with his finger. She screamed and so did I.

'LOUIS, please stop it. Can you open the gate? *Thank god we're home* I thought. I passed Louis the key to the sliding gate so he could open it. Wilson, our builder, had now finished our patio making a huge difference to our property; it now looked larger at the front of our house, and certainly tidier. We were now able to park three cars on the driveway. Before the work was completed, out the front was full of clay mud and weeds.

We'd met Wilson through our neighbour, Sandra. I think she took pity on him one day. He was out touting for business, and only spoke Spanish. He was a short, chubby looking fellow. Sandra obviously spoke the language and asked him for a quote on our behalf. This was within our budget, so the job was his. Finally the driveway was completed. I was excited to show Louis inside where welcoming birthday balloons were scattered everywhere, some pinned up, the rest floating around the room at their own desire. I had blown them up earlier with the unsolicited, support of my darling three year old. She thought all the balloons belonged to her, so after several reminders, she then accepted it was Louis's birthday and not hers. We made a compromise: she was permitted to keep at least one balloon. It was difficult to make arrangements for Michael to join us as a family that evening or any other evening. He had to work the bar, the business was new to us and it was our livelihood and wasn't to be taken lightly.

'I thought we could go to the *Chicken Hut* for dinner tonight, dad can't come cause he's working but he's got tomorrow off.' The *Chicken Hut* was the British nickname for a Spanish restaurant that specialised in barbeque chicken which was flamed, and grilled in front of you, whilst turning on a very large spit roast. The chicken was heavily seasoned with oregano and garlic. Other meat dishes were also available, so it was more of a steak house. It was within walking distance from our house - great for me, I could then have a drink. The restaurant was family run and very reasonably priced. On weekends it had live music which I could hear from my home and I could also enjoy the therapeutic smell of chicken. On Saturdays reservations were necessary. The restaurant was very popular with all nationalities but mainly with the Spanish especially the older generation, as the music was Latin, salsa and ballroom. The Spanish took this kind of dancing seriously; it was very pleasant to watch.

I had now resigned myself to the fact that he was going through a typical teenage stage of life. Louis didn't seem too impressed with his birthday gifts, as he hadn't said otherwise. We took him to our local Chinese restaurant for his birthday, as this was his choice. Chinese food here in Spain is very different to what we have in England: the noodles are soggy, more like spaghetti; it all tastes very sweet and the sauces are more of a liquid which after a while begin to taste the same; the chicken is fried and chewy, never tender. Having said this, it's a very cheap meal here in Spain.

'So son, what you having? Don't tell me Chicken balls?' Michael always joked with Louis. He was pleased to have the evening off but he still had to cash up and lock up, so he limited himself to drink drank coke all night. Anne had offered to look after the bar, she was a godsend and we trusted her but Michael felt responsible to lock up.

'I'm having chicken balls Daddy, the same as Lou, Lou.'

'Are you babe?' Michael then looked towards me. 'What you having babe?' He grabbed my knee. This was the first intimate contact we'd had since moving to Spain. It made my heart flutter; I'd forgotten how this felt. Both of us had been so wrapped up in our own worlds, dealing with the changes in our life, we had forgotten about US. Somehow, I felt this wasn't going to get any better.

The evening passed very quickly as we caught up with one another as much as possible, this included Michael and me as by now I had realised what a sacrifice we had taken on. Twenty four seven, we were separated most of the time; I had not anticipated the hours involved in owning a bar; it had taken over our lives, especially our private life. Someone once said 'Three years was the estimated period for running a bar in Spain'. I thought at the time *That's ridiculous, everyone's different.* Honestly, I think there was truth in this theory, in the majority of most cases. Financially, it paid the bills - just about.

Our next lot of visitors were Snowball, Zoe and their two children who arrived from the north of England the same week as Louis. Snowball was a childhood, and lifelong friend of Michael's. At the time I felt that it was good to have familiar faces around, especially to help

Louis settle in. Also joining us at the weekend was Matt and Lisa. They were all Michael's marching band friends whom I had enjoyed getting to know each time we met up. So it was a full house once again.

I had more or less unpacked most of the boxes by now leaving only a few but there was no rush, so I stored them under the beds, unnoticed. My VW Beetle convertible had also arrived all in one piece at a cost of five hundred pounds cash deal for delivery from Essex to Spain. This car was my pride and joy, cream in colour with a black soft-top roof and alloy wheels. I had taken out a loan the size of a mortgage to pay for the car. Per month this was a three hundred and fifty pound luxury debt. It was soon to change!

Snowball, Zoe and the kids decided to stay in an apartment only five minutes from the bar. This was more suitable for them with several shops and bars within walking distance, plus there was a large swimming pool and playground on the urbanisation. The kids, Harris then seven and Lara ten, were delighted with the beach dead opposite and Snowball wasn't far from his friend. Although time passes between each visit their friendship never altered. In the early days, Michael and Snowball both belonged to the local marching band, *The Blue Eagles*. Snowball was eight years Michael's junior, he played trumpet, Michael was brass instructor. Regularly Michael would pick Snowball up and take him to band practice and then home after a customary trip to the pub in Long Riding. Snowball would sit in the car and wait with the occasional coca cola and bag of crisps. In time this routine changed with Snowy following in those Blackford footsteps, drinking, socialising and entertaining, something he enjoys still to this day.

Michael had joined the marching band at the age of eight in 1971; he played various instruments but the trumpet was his favourite. He taught and arranged music for his band as well as for various other marching bands nationally. Besides getting married to band members, Michael soon became director of The *Blue Eagles* building it to become the most successful band in the country winning seven national championships within eight years, after which it was time for Michael to retire, Unhappily, the band then folded.

'So then boy are you happy?' Snowy asked whilst he sipped his beer. Snowy, Snowball was a nickname given to him since childhood, because of his hair, which was as white as snow, however, both his children's were blonde as was Zoe. His real name was Tony by which Zoe referred to him.

'Yeah, ask me in a year's time though. Did you know Matt and Lisa are coming out at the weekend?' Michael said also sipping his beer. Both the lads had been reminiscing all morning, while I had been cleaning the bar after cooking several breakfasts. It was great to see Michael relaxed and enjoy the company of his best friend. I knew they would have lots to talk about.

'Now there's someone I haven't seen for years, how is he?' Snowball asked.

'His fine mate, got himself a lovely girlfriend, Lisa. You'll like her.'

Snowball had moved to Yorkshire several years ago where he'd met Zoe through the marching band. She was a Yorkshire lass; he fell in love and married her.

'Hi Zoe, you alright, you look a bit red, how's the beach?' I asked. I was drying up glasses as we didn't have a dishwasher, so everything was washed manually. Zoe and the kids now all walked in to the bar covered in sand. Zoe had her arms full: beach bag in one and wet towels in the other hand. Lara held the lilo; Harris was still deep in concentration with his Nintendo clasped in his hands not noticing anything around him other than the next level in his game.

'Great, the kids want to hire *pedalos*. Where do we go?' Michael had fetched the broom at this point to sweep up.

'Just opposite, they do them.' I answered.

'Oh, sorry, that's us with the sand. Leave it there, I'll sweep up when we leave, Michael.'

'No probs, Michael's used to sweeping up the sand. What do you want to drink Zoe? Your tan looks like it's coming on.' I said looking her up and down.

'I know it's a bit red. I'll have a coke and the kids will have lemonade, if that's alright Jo?' Zoe joined Snowball at the bar, the kids sat out on the terrace. I fetched the drinks and then remembered it being Fiesta Week.

'It's the bull run fiesta this week,'

'What's that Jo?'

'It's where they run the bulls in to a large arena, and tease and bait the bull into the sea, in Denia. It's meant to be good fun, every day there's something on. I'll find out more.'

'Yeah, that sounds good, they don't harm the bull, do they?'

'No, I don't think so, sometimes the bull falls in to the sea.' I had only seen the bull run in La Xara, a small village just outside of Denia. There, they had young bulls and they just chased them up and down a street that was sealed off with metal bars and frames, protecting the houses and shops fronts, as well as protecting the public viewing the spectacle. Each village holds their own bull run fiesta, taking it in turn from July to September.

'Will you come and get a day off?'

'Sorry Zoe, we haven't got anyone to cover for us. You guys can go. We'll try and get an evening off when Matt and Lisa arrive. Louis will want to go.' It was difficult working when you had lots of visitors, who were on holiday but sadly we weren't; I had already taken loads of time off to be with the family, and we had to watch our money now.

'Oh that's a shame. Yeah, we can take Louis, can't we Tony?' Zoe asked. So it was arranged. *Bous a la Mar* (Bulls in the Sea).

As far I was concerned, the bulls nearly always stayed on the dry land and it was the participants who teased the bull were the ones that ended up in the sea, or came worst off. The ambulance crew are always onsite and prepared for the wounded. Every year in June, a few weeks before the event held in July, a large metal arena is constructed around the water's edge at Denia's harbour front with a high tiered platform of bench seats based above metal iron barred cages for protection of the audience or for anyone foolish enough to participate in the tormenting the bull. In the centre of the arena is a wooden stage structure of steps being another safety platform for participants. Often, the bull climbs up on top of this to reach the nearest fool that's teasing it at that time. It is a popular fiesta and never short of victims. Boats of all sizes anchor themselves in the sea around the event for a better view. This fiesta goes on for a week; the bulls enter the arena twice a day, normally lunchtime and evening.

Matt and Lisa arrived only for the weekend. They stayed with us, and enjoyed the privacy of upstairs with an en-suite and a large balcony in which to sunbathe, with views of Monte Pego.

Love her! Very white, so white that the minute she stepped on to Spanish soil, she burnt. Matt was a guy I had only met twice, but he had a lot of history with Michael, just like another thousand other band members, or so it seemed to me. I think Michael was famous in his marching days.

Both couples and kids were now settled into their holiday with sunshine and Sangria. Snowball had taken up a routine with the family during the day and in the evening; his nights mostly ended with his friend Michael after Zoe took the kids back to the apartment. This soon changed once Matt and Lisa arrived. It was fiesta time, so there was a lot going on in Denia: live music, fire-crackers, fireworks, and street entertainers.

'So, mum, when's Snowball getting here?' Louis nagged, eager to see the Bull Run. Lisa and Matt had already arrived at our bar, and had sat themselves down with a jug of Sangria while they waited.

'Here they are, so stop your nagging and don't let Sarina hear or she'll want to go.' I didn't want Sarina to go to the Bull Run as I wasn't sure of the dangers there at that time, if any, as I had never been to this particular fiesta. Thoughts of runaway bulls came to mind, notwith-standing my uncontrollable daughter. Although Zoe had offered to take her, I felt this would not be fair on anyone. It would have been a disaster if they had; I could see it now, Zoe returning with a screaming child out of control, whom I had not disciplined, having given into her for an easy life, as it was convenient for me at that time without realising that rod I had begun to make for myself.

'So are we ready or shall we have a drink first'? Asked Snowball.

'Yeah come and have a drink first. Matt and Lisa still have some Sangria left to drink. What do you fancy? I'll get them.' Michael offered and reached for a beer glass to serve Snowball first. I already had a glass of wine, my usual reward after I finished the morning's work when I could relax with the thought of no more breakfasts or lunches to cook, especially for large parties of people when I always worried about forgetting someone's meal or if the food wasn't hot enough. As for the cooking, my biggest concern was not to break an egg. This was my major problem; I could have a frying pan with two successfully shaped eggs in it and then I'd crack another egg which would fall on top of the cooked ones. Try and separate them! It's like separating Siamese twins. The end result would be to throw them out, so some mornings I could easily break ten eggs when I only needed to cook four; egg wastage was my domain.

Everyone finished their drinks, leaving Sarina behind with me in the bar, she was happy interrogating a customer as to what she had in her handbag, oblivious to the fact that everyone had left for the fiesta; she was in search for a good result, a lipstick, an addition to a large collection stashed away back home.

'Have a good time. Do you have money Lou?' I called out as they all strolled off together, chattering with excitement about watching the bulls, heading towards Denia, leaving their hire cars behind. Parking was impossible this time of year.

'Yes, mother.' The bar was now left empty and quiet, apart from the couple with whom Sarina was still occupied, nice people from Leeds, who were here on a month's holiday, now semi-retired, and dividing their time between both countries. They owned an apartment behind the bar somewhere. (I was still familiarising myself with the area,). Both were similar in looks and very well suited in personality, jovial. I stuck around to keep Michael company and to wait for the return of our visitors.

'I see you didn't clean the *plancha* like I do.' Oh here we go, Michael was now about to nag and dictate to me on how to clean a *plancha*. 'If you wipe it with kitchen towel whilst it's still hot it's easier to clean.'

'Yes Michael, I know and I did that.'

'No you didn't, I can tell there's still grease on it.' *Oh fuck off* went through my mind. Such a perfectionist, nothing I do is to his standard when it comes to cleaning; no wonder I was his fourth wife.

Louis returned buzzing as did everyone else. He enjoyed the company and mentioned that while they queued he could hear the anger of the bulls behind the metal doors separating them from the arena. Horns bashed at the doors that confronted them. Sadly, they weren't allowed into the arena and view the event because Lara and Harris were too young. But they enjoyed the buzz of Denia. So instead they visited the hippy market, situated just opposite the port harbour, where the arena was assembled. The hippy market is an assortment of little wooden colourful huts; that sells mainly jewellery and handbags, at reasonable prices, offering the designer copies close enough to the real thing. The girls made several purchases. Hair braiding was also mentioned, it taking place behind the huts. *Probably to save on space? Or was it an illegal service?* The hair braiding was offered by the African women who were in competition with one another. Sarina has had her hair braided on several occasions there, but when finished, she looks almost Chinese they tightly braid the hair. Each time she's had this done I have to take it out after a couple of days because she complains of a headache. Not a service I think I could pursue!

The evening soon drew in. We all went out for dinner and caught up with the day's activities. Sarina was now in pocket with three lipsticks and nurtured them whilst we all sat and drank. Michael had arranged cover in the bar for a couple of hours; Anne had volunteered: 'Go on, it's quiet. Everyone's in Denia with the fiestas, I'll be ok for a few hours.' We struggled at first to find a restaurant that suited us all, especially one for Lisa as she was a vegetarian, and there weren't many restaurants in the area that catered for her. Fish yes, but a NO, for Michael. Eventually we agreed on one, pizza it was. The boys caught up and reminisced while we girls drank wine. It was nearing the end of a nice holiday as the next day they all left for England, except for our Louis.

* * Quality time with the kids? * *

I woke up with a headache. Sarina was nagging at me to get up, Louis had the telly blaring and Michael had left to open the bar that morning. He was on his own until I could grace him with my presence, which at this rate, wasn't going to be for a few hours. 'Can't you both go swimming and give me a break?'

'Come on Chucky, let's leave her in peace, go and get your armbands.' An offer Sarina couldn't refuse as it wasn't often that he obliged. After they had been gone for a couple of hours, I was thinking I'd best check on them just as Sarina came running to the back door, soaked from the swimming pool, leaving dirty foot prints on the dusty patio; it needed to be hosed daily because of the dust from the building site opposite.

A young skinny lad, my height, was two steps behind her.

'Hello, Sarina slow down, careful before you slip.' Something she normally did on a daily basis.

'Hello, I'm Billy, we have a house here.'

'That's nice, I'm Jo, are you on holiday? Or do you live here?'

'We're on holiday, me, me brother, mum and dad'
Damn, I thought, *a lad similar in age to Louis, would have been great if they lived here.*

'Mum, I'm just getting the lilo'. Sarina was now pushing past me to get to her bedroom in search for a punctured lilo.

'Sarina, there's one in the shed. Where's Lou?'

'Oh, he's by the pool with me mum, dad and brother.' With that, we all left for the pool.

'So Billy, how old are you?' I asked as we walked to the pool area, which was barely four seconds away,

'Thirteen, and me brother's fifteen'. There was Louis, sat chatting with his feet in the swimming pool.

'Hi mum, this is Charley, Annie and Tom.'

'Hello, you must be Jo, nice to meet you. Louis has been telling us all about you, buying a bar here, sounds exciting.' *It does,* I thought, *Louis has actually acknowledged the bar, and our big move.* I joined Louis by the pool, into which Sarina jumped now armed with a lilo as well as her armbands; for a three year-old, she was ballsy. She splashed both Louis and me as she leapt in; she was happy. Billy then followed with a bigger splash this time. 'Billy, careful, you've just splashed Jo and Louis.' Luckily my hair is naturally curly but it was now splattered to the side of my face; I put my fingers through it and shook it to separate the wet curls.

'Sorry,' he shouted, and then swam off to join Sarina. The heat of the sun was burning my back whilst I sat in conversation with our new neighbours. Nice family - Annie was a school secretary, Tom was a gardener. Very genuine people and I liked them instantly. Two hours passed.

'Sorry, I have to go. I have to take over from Michael,' whom I'd forgotten about; 'nice to meet you. Come on Sarina.'

'Do I have to? Can't I stay with Lou Lou please?'

'She's alright I'll watch her'. Louis was obviously trying to impress this family, he wouldn't normally have offered to have his pesky little sister, but I guess he could see she was having fun with Billy, which didn't put him out too much.

Michael was not amused. 'Where have you been? I've done twelve breakfasts whilst you've been in bed, where's Sarina?'

'At home with Louis, she's got a new friend.' Once Michael had calmed down about my late arrival, I told him about our new neighbours who were here for a month's holiday. Not that he was too interested, his mind was occupied with the bar, checking everything was in place and well stocked up, that the two soft drinks fridges behind the bar, as well as the large chest freezer in the kitchen was stocked with the readymade meals, chips steak and fish etc. We offered a small snack menu during the day, and a varied selection of meals in the evening. Fresh produce was bought daily for the fridge. Nothing went to waste even if it meant me taking it home for lunch or dinner.

'How's Louis?' Michael asked with concern. He knew Louis wasn't happy with the idea of two and a half months with us without his mates. I had hoped he would help behind the bar, but no, he was too shy for this and was not in the least bit interested.

'Well, he's got a couple of mates now for a month so that should help'. And it did. We barely saw Louis, he was out every day with the boys and their parents who were doing some kind of activity, from go karting, eating out, going to the beach to just relaxing by the swimming pool. This suited both families; I also enjoyed their company, as did Michael. Sarina especially enjoyed Billy's company as he kept her amused. Both Annie and Tom were also very patient with her demands. Nothing was too much trouble for this family; they were always very willing and able.

I dreaded their departure, which was soon to come. Louis would be bored and would want to return to England.

'Are you ready to go? Sarina come here; let me brush your hair.' Sarina strode over with her hands attached to her head. 'Sarina put your hands down or you're not going out for dinner.' Louis then walked in through the back door, not amused with the idea of dinner with his three year old sister and mother. He had the upstairs room with the en-suite. This suited all of us as he had his privacy and peace.

'So where's this restaurant we're going to, and how long are we gonna be?'

'It's in Els poblets, and it's called *The Orange Grove*. Can you lock the back door Lou? Right, where's the kitten?' The kitten was a recent purchase from the cat's home. It was colourful tabby cat. We called her Isabel, after our bank manager.

The cat's refuge is in Denia, along an unmade road, quite awkward to find. It was a derelict building; it once was the station house. I believe the mayor had granted permission for the refuge to be sited there on the condition that if a time came when they were asked to leave, they would do so straight away with no fuss or any petitions. We had to make a donation for the kitten that I felt was fair given they had to feed all those cats and kittens. There were quite a few there. It was a full house.

The cats' home is funded by a charity shop in Els Poblets, (in English this means *The Small Village*), and indeed it is a small village, very old and in need of modernising. It's not a pretty village, very old and grey, built up with lots of terraced houses and some shops. Even nowadays one can still see clothes washing pegged and hung out across some of the properties; on occasion one can glimpse the odd elderly senora dressed in black, sweeping outside the front of her home. On the outskirts of the village the properties are more modern, inhabited by lots of Germans, a few Dutch and some Spanish. Soon the area will be taken over by the Brits with the help of more construction.

Volunteers work in the charity shop selling mainly second-hand clothes and brick a brac, but it does surprisingly well. It also gives retired women and a few men a place in which to work where they can exercise their pre-retirement skills in sales and management. I think it may well also be a refuge to escape their spouses and a place to socialise.

'Isabel's asleep on your bed,' shouted Louis, whilst he locked the back door leaving the key in the lock as we always did. It was just the three of us going out to dinner; Michael was in his usual place, the bar.

The drive to *The Orange Grove* was a pleasant one, only ten minutes in the car through the village of Els Poblets, then onto a country road that leads to Denia. The restaurant was just off this road. Citrus fruit trees grew on either side of the road, most of it fenced off to keep their groves secure. In my thoughts whilst I drove, was the name of the restaurant, The Orange Grove: what a good name, very appropriate for its position along this road. And yes, there was plenty of orange groves surrounding it, I noticed as I pulled into the shingle car park, parking next door to a skip overflowing with rubbish. 'Here we are.'

The restaurant had only been open for two months, so I guess there was lots of clearing out to do. 'Is this it? Looks empty,'

'Yes Louis, we are early,' I replied as I unplugged Sarina from her car seat and then lifted her out onto the shingled earth, not great for the platform shoes that I was wearing that evening, all dolled up with my bronze tan and red shiny lip gloss. I felt quite good about myself and it was a shame that Michael wasn't with us. We approached the restaurant with me hanging onto Sarina for support because of my high heels. To my surprise we came face to face with a rather large, tatty looking German Shepherd. Sarina jumped into my arms nearly toppling me over; there was no way I could run with these shoes and hold onto Sarina; I had more chance at survival by taking them off and throwing them at the dog; this would have been sure to have knocked him out.

'He's ok,' shouted a scruffy looking man, who came out from the restaurant to greet us, or rescue us, I wasn't sure which at the time. The dog ignored us; he was old and not interested. Apparently, he had come with the restaurant and was part of the fixtures and fittings for the new owners. Not a great advert I thought, especially where food, health, hygiene and safety were concerned. The dog needed a week's stay at a beauty parlour.

'Hello, are you open?'

'Yeah, sure. How many of you?' as he looked for the fourth member of our family.

'Just the three of us,' I answered awkwardly.

'Do you want to sit inside or out?'

'Outside please, we're British, we need the sun.'

(or what was left of it as the evening was drawing in).

We sat down on the wooden Spanish chairs with a table to match, almost antique. I looked around to check out the environment: lots of dark wood and large mirrors, as well as an open fire that was in desperate need of a clean. The restaurant stood alone with no neighbours, with only the sound of the passing traffic, otherwise quite peaceful. The outside area was full of blossom and a couple of trees that held two glorious white rope hammocks. This finished off the outside quite nicely.

Sarina just couldn't help herself once she had spotted these swinging chairs, so up she leapt, followed by Louis; they sat and swung in them.

'Here are the menus, today's specials are on the board. Do you want a drink?'

'Yes please,' I ordered the drinks and then began my interrogation, 'So is this your restaurant?'

'Yes, it's mine and Jean's, that's my wife'. As if by clockwork, out popped Jean from the kitchen. She wiped her hands down the front of her pinny and greeted me with a hand shake. We made our introductions. She was a short, skinny woman, very pleasant with long blonde hair in desperate need of a haircut, as was her husband's whose hair was so long he had pulled it back into a ponytail. This look's OK in your twenties, possibly even thirties but late fifties? No, get a life. Yet I had noticed a lot of older men who lived here had this style with their hair, whereas the women had scraped their hair up and back off their faces. *No, this was not going to reduce the wrinkles.* I think these people had moved abroad and had wanted to relive their youth again - someone needs to tell them!

Jean had been a teacher as had her husband, John. They had both retired early to start a restaurant business in Spain amongst the orange groves; it sounded like a dream come true.

We chatted for a while, exchanged a few helpful hints on being in business in Spain, ordered our food and then waited. 'How much longer mum? I'm starving.'

'Louis, sit down and wait,' he stood from his chair, now agitated.

'Well, you haven't stopped talking, I'm bored and hungry, and can we have some more *alioli* and bread?' A traditional Spanish starter, alioli is a mayonnaise made mainly from garlic and olive oil served with sliced French stick bread and sometimes comes with fresh, crushed tomatoes. Each restaurant has its own way of making it. Our food finally arrived, and as we were all starving, it made the meal taste so much nicer; we left nothing but empty plates. Sarina returned back to the swinging chair; she was so amused that had now decided she wanted one.

'Lou, Lou push me, come on.'

'I'll do it.' I got up, giving Louis a look of disapproval. He was bored and all he wanted to do was to return home and meet up with the boys. Sweat had dried and stuck to me, the evening sun was still hot, and I hobbled over to Sarina in my unforgiving shoes. John had just begun to clear away the plates when Jean arrived with a chocolate Magnum for Sarina. She had nagged all evening for an icecream, so her reward had finally arrived. Her face lit up as Jean unwrapped the lolly, then handed it over. 'What do you say?' I asked.

'Thank-you.'

'Lou, do you want one?'

'No I'm alright.' He sniggered. He was being impatient and rude. I ordered a coffee whilst Sarina devoured her lolly. I felt angry about Louis's sulking behaviour. *Why had I bothered to take him out for dinner, when he was so unappreciative.* 'Mum, look.' Louis shouted and pointed towards his sister. *What now,* I thought, *if I hear mum mentioned once more I'm going to kill.* There she sat covered in chocolate, she had not only eaten the icecream she was also wearing it as was Jean's new white swing chair. It was time to leave.

'Don't worry,' she exclaimed. 'I can wash it.'

'I'm so sorry.' Luckily I had some baby wipes in my handbag. Sarina was covered, her hands, her dress, her face, she was a sight. I also felt so guilty and embarrassed about the swing chair. And upset with Louis's attitude. It was now a good time to leave. *This couple will never forget us.*

* * The robberies * *

The drive home was very quiet, Louis had now stopped his nagging and Sarina was asleep in her car seat, head tilted to one side with chocolate dribbling from the corner of her mouth.

As we pulled up in front of the gate to our house, I stopped the car abruptly. 'Louis, is that the kitten on the wall?'

'Shit, Mum, sorry to swear, but, that cat was asleep inside.'

'Right, stay calm and stay in the car.' I ordered firmly. I needed a weapon. *What could I use to protect myself?* I thought whilst I searched the back of my car. 'Lou pass me that umbrella, stay here with your sister and lock the car.'

'Mum, what are you going to do with an umbrella? And I'm comin' with ya.' I now felt myself becoming angry.

'Louis, do as you're told, stay here, your sister needs you.' With that I left the car still parked in the middle of the road with both my kids inside. I walked over to my neighbours first, pressed their buzzer and looked over my shoulder to check Louis was still in the car. Typically, the neighbours they were out, *It's Thursday* I thought, *they always go out on Thursdays*. I unlocked the gate to my drive way and slowly slid the gate open, and then walked towards my front door; I couldn't hear or see anything suspicious. Now I approached the front door, placed my key in to the lock and turned it once.

'Mum, come back to the car, let's call dad.' Louis now stood next to me with his three year-old sister half asleep in his arms.

'Louis.' I shouted, 'What are you doing? Go back to the flippin car.' Now I had lost it, both my children were now in as much danger as I was. Louis saw the fear in my face, he walked back towards our gate sheepishly, at which precise moment my neighbours Sandra and Toni, having returned from their evening out, had pulled up next to my car. Louis went straight over to them. I meanwhile proceeded to turn the key once again, the final turn that unlocked the door. Shock hit me: my back door was hanging off its hinges, with the glass eased out of its frame. First, I felt panicked. *What have they taken?* I couldn't see any destruction apart from the back door. *Shit, what if they're still here?* Just as that thought entered my head and still armed with my umbrella, Toni arrived.

'Everything ok Jo?' he asked, as he passed me, in search of the robbers with a large heavy torch in his hand, firmly held ready for an attack; it certainly wasn't for illumination, as it was still light outdoors, just about to turn from dimness to darkness.

The property was empty, no mess and no robbers, only Toni and me. We looked at each other and then our 'weapons'; we were more armed for the weather and light of day, than for an intruder.

The house was left tidy, they had known where to go. I guess it was the usual place most people kept their gadgets, the wardrobe. My video camera, a digital camera that had only been replaced a few months back together with my mobile phone were gone. No jewellery was missing; maybe we had disturbed them.

Sandra had raised the alert, by calling the police (La Guardia).

'My neighbour has been robbed; she is alone with a small infant. Please come immediately.' Sandra assured me that if she hadn't mentioned Sarina being a baby, then they wouldn't have come. Because of the high percentage of robberies, the police normally prefer for the victims to report the incident at their station. Children and old people seem to take preference. The Spanish respect their elderly; there are very few old peoples' homes here in Spain. They prefer to look after their own making this one of the reasons their properties are kept so long in their families, passed down from one generation to another. I believe this is why they are close as a family unit. They love children and their time is always given to them. You'll always see Spanish children out are always out late with their families, having an evening meal, in restaurants and bars; they are welcome everywhere. I believe this helps children with their social skills, learning how to behave and grow up respectfully when out in company. A contrast to being dumped with the babysitter, left alone at home or on the street to fend for themselves, or, as a last resort, being sent to sit in the family room, treated like social outcasts.

Within ten minutes two police cars arrived with sirens; this alerted a couple of neighbours. Charley and Billy were around in a flash. 'Hi Jo, what's going on?' Louis caught their attention and walked over to them with Sarina, her hands still clasped around his neck, like a chimpanzee. I now joined Sandra and Toni, who were informing the police as to what had happened. I felt myself get upset. *Where was Michael while this was going on? Of course in that stupid bar, that had become his new home.* He seemed never to be around when needed.

The police were very sympathetic. They too searched the property and asked me some questions relevant to the robbery. I answered them standing by the damaged back door, and then I noticed the key in the lock. The robbers had obviously tried to wedge the door off its hinges, but when they noticed the key it would be an easier option to wedge the glass out of its frame and then use the key. How stupid of me, my attitude needed to change, this was our second robbery. The first one was at Alicante airport, less than a year ago.

Our first robbery was in Alicante in 2004. We had

been on a return visit to Spain to finalise a few things with the property and were on our way home. It was five o'clock in the morning, and it was raining. We had just pulled in to the car park at Alicante airport searching for the car hire company from which we had hired our car. 'There it is Michael over there to your right, there's a space park there.' And so he did.

'Right, I'll go get a trolley, you sort Sarina out.' It was still dark at this hour of the morning. *Sunday! Shit, back to work tomorrow* I thought, taking Sarina's push chair from the boot of the car. As usual, she was asleep from the journey and the early start; I was also tired, still not fully focused. First, I set the push chair up, unplugging Sarina's seat belt slowly so as not to wake her. On the other side of the car, Michael had returned with a trolley and began to load our cases on to it; he placed our flight bag in its usual place, at the front of the trolley. Now loaded, he left the trolley by the boot of the car. He then returned to the back seat of the hire car to collect some rubbish: an odd crisp bag of Sarina's and a couple of empty drink cartons, (he had asked me to dothis).

'No, can't you see I'm busy, leave it.' I stressed, now tucking Sarina comfortably into her pushchair.

'No Jo, I'm not a slob like you, I'll do it.' Whilst doing so, neither of us had noticed the black BMW slowly drive passed us. He returned back from the bin and in a panicked voice, he asked,

'Have you got the flight bag?'

'No, you have.' I explained, and then I wheeled Sarina round to his side of the car.

'Shit, it's gone!'

'It can't have, there's no one around except us.' I searched around the car frantically.

'The black BMW, it was loitering around us, they've taken it. Didn't you see it?'

'What BMW?' I asked, 'I didn't see one.' I hadn't because I was too busy bent over Sarina, carefully laying her down into her pushchair whilst she slept.

'It was parked my side of the car, I just thought they were looking for a parking place. Shit they were watching me; they must have taken it when I bent into the car to get your rubbish!'

'My rubbish? Fuckin' hell, what are we going to do?'

'Jo, the flight tickets were in there, passports, money, not much though. Do you have any? Shit, the credit cards, Spanish cheque book, oh shit and I left the pin number with it all!' Of course I took the situation into hand. I became hysterical and cried. 'I'll call the bank,' Michael said, 'shit, I can't, my phone was in there, and my camera you bought me for my 40th.'

'Stop it, right now, I've got my phone. I'll call the bank, no I can't, it's Sunday, they'd be closed, they'll have an emergency number.' So I began to call, then panic set in again. 'It's all in Spanish; I can't bloody well speak Spanish.' With that Michael took the phone from me.

'I'll call Ron, he's fluent and he'll call the bank.' Which Ron did.

We made our way to *Easy Jet's* customer counter; we informed them about what had happened. They were very good to us and gave us a printout substitute to our boarding passes and then directed us to the police to report the theft.

It took a while to find the police office. And when we did, we thought we'd found the janitor. A rather large man wearing a waffle cardigan, was standing outside a white temporarily partitioned wall; he led us through a door that was part of this structure, into a small room. Here, he took off his waffle cardigan that then displayed a police uniform; both Michael and I glanced at each other. He was the policeman and this is the police office? He sat us down and asked where and when it happened and what was taken. He spoke only Spanish but we found a way to answer his questions. He then pulled out an antique typewriter to type out the report; the keys were long and old, and as he pushed each key for a letter it took a while for the letter to print and for the key to return to position. This was going to take a while; I felt as though I was in a Will Haye movie *'Ask A Policeman'* but no, this was the real deal. So here we were with no passport, no tickets, our personal belongings stolen, no access to a bank and five euros in change. Not to mention a manually typed police report that should be in a museum. But this report from antiquity did see us on board our return flight back to England.

In 2005 we had a replay of our first robbery. I needed to toughen up if I was to live in this country. I felt scared after the robbery, it had frightened me, I had sleepless nights on the sofa awaiting Michael to return from the bar in the early hours of the morning. The thought that someone had entered my home disturbed me, *What if we were in at the time, would they still have come?* Michael returned home a little earlier that night of the robbery. I felt as though I'd put him out by asking him to come home. Little sympathy was spared; I just had to get on with it.

A few weeks after the incident Louis returned back to England to begin his college course in Carpentry. Also Annie, Tom and the boys left, their holiday having come to an end. This upset me; I was again left home alone at night with Sarina. I knew I would miss Louis but it was his future we had to consider. Was it all worth it, moving here?

* * *Sarina's First Day At School* * *

Michael was disappointed that there was no uniform. I was excited about the school hours: nine to five, freedom! Although for the month of September, because of the heat, the schools are only open for half the usual day. Sarina was only three years old and had convinced herself that she was only going to stay at school for a couple of hours and that was it. Sadly she was wrong. I had insisted that Michael was to come with us that first morning to support me and face the mummies. I was as scared as Sarina. My Spanish was only pigeon Spanish; I had recently re-started private lessons to improve on my conversational Spanish, so I could have a basic conversation, but this I found very difficult. Poor old Sarina, there was me thinking only about myself and what Spanish I knew or more accurately, didn't know, when she was about to be thrown in at the deep end of Spanish school.

We had visited the school a month prior and had spoken with the head mistress; she had assured us that due to Sarina's age, she would absorb the language like a sponge and be fluent within six months. I wasn't so sure, but true enough, she was. The school was based in Els Poblets, a small school with a couple of palm trees in the front of the playground. Their dinner hut was a little undesirable, it was like a garden shed at the back of the school. Quite nice inside, the floor was tiled and clean enough; it had wooden benches for seating, but was far too small, enough room to accommodate roughly twenty children. Not many children stayed for *comador* (dinner) as most were picked up by their parents or another family member, even grandma at lunch time and taken home for their siesta of three hours. On occasion an elderly grandma with her Zimmer frame, barely able to walk, would pick up her grandchild from school. The locals were very familiar with and attentive to the elderly, in case they needed assistance; meanwhile, the youngsters always seemed to behave agreeably on these rare occasions. After the month of September the children return back to school starting at three o'clock and leaving at five. This is the routine until the month of June, when the school once again reverts back to half days. I noticed most of the mums were housewives who didn't work, and were of a similar age to myself, between mid thirtys and forty.

The lolly pop man, a policeman, was on patrol every morning escorting the children safely across the road. He had arrived with the school cleaner that first morning. She took her mop, bucket and tray of cleaning accessories from the back of his car. Michael and I were astonished; we looked at each other and thought alike, *I can just imagine back home in England, an English policeman offering a lift to one of the cleaners at the local school in his patrol car. How sweet* I thought. This was why I had wanted to move here, it was like living back in the 60s or 70s, within a small village, where everyone knew each other, more or less, and had grown up there, and so had their parents and their parents before them.

The children started to arrive, all different in age and size up to eleven or twelve years. The school was only a small school; it held up to a hundred children, mixed nationalities but mainly Spanish. Only a small number, maybe eight or so of the children approximately, were English. We didn't notice any English mums there that morning, only a little chubby Spanish boy holding on to the school's fence for dear life. His father tried to pull him away and his mother shouted at him in Spanish; obviously it was his first day too. Sarina clutched to her dad's neck, taking in her new environment with big open eyes as we walked in to the school playground. As parents we were allowed to enter the school classroom, to see our children to their seats, to hang up their school bag and then run!

We were the last parents to leave that morning; again, I felt sick but it wasn't as bad as the time I first took her to nursery. That I will never forget. Not having given in to Sarina during her nursery days made her first day at school a lot easier. She only cried crocodile tears for two or three days. As we left the school, one of the mums came over to us, an attractive woman with naturally curly hair. She was Spanish, but spoke to us in English. 'What time do we pick them up do you know?'

'Yes, one o'clock, the school finishes, throughout all of September.' I answered unsure if she understood. We then introduced ourselves: her name was Sandra and she was the mother of Alex who was also in Sarina's class. This made me feel at ease, at least I now knew one person who spoke English in the school. We soon became friends.

As the first few weeks of school passed, I noticed the mums befriend one another; I was never one to become a *mummy mobster,* not with Louis any way. But I felt I should make the effort here and having Sandra as a friend helped. Each morning the mobster mummies dropped their cherubs off and then went for coffee; a couple of times I joined them; and they made me feel very welcome. This also helped improve my Spanish, although on occasion I still got myself into trouble with translating English to Spanish. Once I went to the chemist with ulcers in my mouth, I was in extreme pain. I looked up the word *pain* in the dictionary and accidently picked out *peinier.* I already knew how to say 'I have' and the word *boca* was mouth so I pronounced, *Tengo una peinier en mi boca.* I thought I'd said, 'I have pain in my mouth,' well I hadn't. I had instead said, 'I have a penis in my mouth.' I had thoroughly entertained the woman in the chemist that day as were the mums at the school when Sandra repeated the story on my behalf.

After school the mums would pick up their children and gather round the park opposite the school. There, each child would have a snack of some kind, not sweets or chocolate, mostly a *bocadillo*. This is a sandwich made with a French stick, and in place of butter the Spanish use olive oil and salt, with their choice of filling, for example ham or pork. There was only one child who didn't take a snack, mainly because her mother was always in a rush and was never organised. It was Sarina, but the mobster mummies would never let her go without, she would always be fed with a bread stick or a biscuit of some kind; they were always considerate and shared. I think they understood I was blonde and dizzy with other things on my mind. This was their daily routine, the after school picnic. I attended most days but avoided others. As a professional chatter box it was difficult for me to sit and not talk, to only try understand what was being said, which as a rule was of no interest to me. Sarina would show off if she couldn't go to the park bribery would be the result to make her behave. Blackmail is the final solution to desperation; what else is available when a three-year old with a strong personality, with *Chucky* for a nick name, who threw her weight around without a care in the world. The last thing I needed was to draw attention to myself within this little Spanish village school. During her stay, my mother had warned me to be 'more firm', otherwise her behaviour would only get worse, and it had.

Sarina was very popular with the children and their parents. She was unique, the only English girl in her class, very confident and learnt the language very quickly. The mothers were intrigued by this and often they would tell me that her Spanish was *Moy Bien,* 'very good' and that she spoke the language clearly and correctly. My Spanish improved at the rate of a snail; I really had to work hard at it. The mums were patient with me and understood that I had just recently moved to their country. But how long was I to use this excuse; I could see myself still at the same level in five years hence. Practice was what I needed, but it was difficult because I was habitually around English people.

* * *The scooter* * *

Transport soon became an issue. We only had the one car to help keep our overheads down. The problem was that we used a lot of petrol toing and froing, because Michael had to have the car at the end of the day to lock up the bar. Sometimes this didn't work out and would result in hiring a taxi.

So a decision was made, we took an afternoon off to go and buy a scooter.

We only visited one store in Denia; it was the only one we knew. Exacty what we wanted was there in the window, a black Peugeot scooter, so we entered the store and looked around for assistance. There stood a young lad with glasses very studious looking.

'Hola, hablas ingles?' we asked. This was our commonplace sentence, one that we arrogantly used for nearly two years without any thought of trying to speak the language. We eventually became aware of this and improved our Spanish, not speaking fluently like our daughter, but enough to get by. At the end of the day, we were the foreigners in their country. Imagine going to Tesco to ask the same question, do you speak Spanish?

We Brits would be flabbergasted. The Spanish are a tolerant race, especially here in Denia, as this area is very international.

'Yes, I speak English, Spanish and French.' *Great* I thought, *a shop assistant with languages.*

'But I don't work here.' *Shit we need help,* I thought, now facing a rather large Spanish shop assistant who at the time was shaking his head 'no', he didn't speak English. But with my zest and charm I persuaded the young lad to translate the sale of our scooter. He was a French student, only eighteen, here in Denia on vacation.

After a couple of hours of hard translation and many questions, we soon became the proud owners of a black Peugeot scooter. Paper work was successfully completed. In Spain practically everything one does involves paper work and this is always the main issue; even acquiring a scooter requires a copy of the passport, copy of the NIE (Identification number) all of which must be available at all times including a copy of the *residencia* (certificate of residence) and an up-to-date copy of the *padron* (electoral roll). To begin with, it took us a while to remember all this paper work. We learnt the hard way with several trips home and searching cupboards for documents. Soon we had them all together in a folder and just took the whole thing to be on the safe side. Some or all of these documents may be required to buy a mobile phone, register your daughter at school, open a bank account, purchase an electrical item with a guarantee, collect a parcel, register letter and so on. Without them, the Spanish shrug of the shoulders is the outcome. They didn't care a toot and there was never any leeway. The scooter was a godsend; after having only one form of transport, it made life a little easier for us, and was more affordable with tax and insurance. I wanted to learn to ride on it but after one incident, I gave up. It looked easy enough to do and Michael instructed me on how to ride it. But when it came to switching the bike off, the footrest became an issue; I struggled to sweep my foot strongly enough to slide the damned footrest out, for the bike to rest on. Fuck it I couldn't achieve this. So in anger I laid the bike down and refused ever to ride it again. Michael never ever pushed this any further, maybe it was the pain I caused him in watching me that afternoon, motoring around our complex with him running at my side, at the same speed I was travelling, passing the builders who witnessed and cheered once I gained my speed. That was my first and last time ever to ride a scooter. The scooter became Michael's new company transport.

* * Back to the locals * *

Ten o'clock in the morning I was mopping the floor of the bar. How ugly the floor tiles looked, they never shone, no matter what we used, but we could not afford to replace them. They were the original floor tiles, dark, old and very unattractive. Our lives were now on a budget. Winter was soon to arrive, which meant we had only the locals to depend upon for business. The mornings were now becoming cooler. It was September. The majority of tourists had now left; and it was as if someone had switched off a light switch. It was dead quiet but this was now the time of year for couples arriving for their vacation; the kids had returned back to school so it was now safe. Jenny was outside setting the tables up for breakfast; we had the local radio music blaring out which did not help my huge hangover, the aftermath from the night before.

I'd helped out the previous evening, and worked alongside Lyn. Our regular bingo caller had not turned up, so Michael had to step in. Anne, our cook, babysat Chucky for the evening. I hadn't been out for an evening for a few months so it was well overdue, even if it was bar work, bingo and quiz.

Michael had introduced me to a charming couple, Vincente and Lynda. A nice couple who liked a drink and a good time, a bit like myself. We hit it off straight away. Vincente came from the local village of La Xara, Lynda his wife came from London. She was a real cockney, but, she could also pass as an Essex girl. They had met in London, many years ago. Vincente owned a restaurant there; he was an admirable business man. 'A penny is a Penny, a Pound is a Pound. Look after the pennies, whilst the pounds look after themselves,' he always said, and how true was that. They sold the restaurant and retired to Spain, to harvest their oranges. Vincente, a real character, was short in height with a rosy face. At first I couldn't understand him, but the more I drank, the more I understood. He spoke English faster than his Spanish, and when he got excited, he yelped out loud: 'MEOW.'

That night I think Sarina played Anne up by not going to bed. The signs were there in the morning when I struggled to get her up for school, taking a little longer than normal, but eventually I had accomplished the mission with bribery and blackmail.

That morning my head was pounding, the pain having travelled to the side of my face. I was just thinking it was time for another pain killer when suddenly Party Time Jim walked up the few stairs outside that led on to our terrace and into our bar. At first I almost didn't recognise him.

'Have you seen my wallet?' He was sober, that's why he looked entirely different. It was a Monday, Party Time Jim didn't drink during the week, not whilst he worked. He was an estate agent in Denia, in partnership with an old friend of his.

'When did you lose your wallet?' I asked staring at him and soon became obvious to him. He had only ever come to the bar at weekends, pissed; never had I seen him sober, or even a little tipsy before becoming drunk. He would stagger into the bar, clap his hands and shout, 'Party time,' at the top of his voice, without a care in the world. He would then buy himself a drink and anyone else who cared for his company. This obviously attracted a lot of hangers on. I think he was aware of this but he was too busy drowning in his own sorrows to care. He was good looking, I suddenly noticed, a totally different man sober. He had natural grey flecks in his hair and looked younger that morning. Michael had told me that he didn't drink during the week and only binge drank at weekends.

'Yesterday, so have you seen it? I was here in the afternoon.' *Yes but where were you last night* I thought, *in one of those so-called clubs Michael had told me about.* It was obvious to me: some whore had taken it when Jim was off his head and couldn't remember. Jim often bragged that he visited these clubs at weekends; it never impressed me: why pay for sex, when he could perfectly chat or pull any bird. I guess he didn't want the involvement, the attachment that had possibly caused the hurt he was suffering. No strings attached, no questions asked, no answers, just sex for a price. Possibly a cheaper price than dating a girl.

'Jo have you seen it?' He shouted.

'Oh. No sorry Jim.' He broke my thoughts. And then he left abruptly. I'd hoped he would have stayed for a coffee but I think he knew what I was thinking and felt uncomfortable. I would have interrogated him about his drinking. *What a waste* I thought. Then Denzel walked in for his usual, an alcohol free beer.

'Morning Denzel, how are you?' He grunted, held the white square patch that covered his voice box with two fingers, just below his Adams apple. Then spoke, huskily, *'cerveza.'* There was no answer to my question, but a nod was sufficient enough. He drank alcohol-free beer as was his habit and due to ill health. Denzel was a retired pub landlord who had indulged in the luxuries of life; booze and fags. Now retired to Spain, he had given up smoking and alcohol but just kept the one habit, his bar visits socially on a regular basis. One always knew when Denzel was off visiting a bar, his fold-up chair would sit abandoned on the beach until his return. No one dared to touch it.

What was I doing here, I thought to myself that morning, *passing the time of day with piss heads or people with problems. Why had we come here?* I asked myself. The dream was: healthy living in the sunshine – yes, I guess Michael, Sarina and I had great tans; relaxing on the beach with my family - yes, on occasion we were all together but Michael he was always in the bar, working; Sarina learning another language and culture - another yes, she was settling in well with school and learning the language at a good pace; life and work in a slower rat race - that was a definite no. We were now working longer hours for less pay, but if that was the price to pay for sunshine, so be it. *I hope my frame of mind doesn't change,* I thought, *we have given up so much to be here and I'm not prepared to let that go, no matter what the cost.*

Conner had now arrived. Shit, he owed us a hundred euros; his drink tab was at its limit. Michael and I had both agreed to ask him for payment, but who was going to ask him for the money? Michael and Conner had a certain understanding, so I left the worrying task with him. But what was I going to say for now? 'Hi Conner,' I picked up a couple of dirty glasses, avoiding eye contact, hoping he was going to mention his bill first. *Damn Michael, I knew this would happen; he always leaves me with the dirty work.*

'Hi Jo, can I have a pint and how much do I owe at the moment?' good question I thought, I hate to ask anyone for money. I knew exactly the amount, but nevertheless I picked up the pad that showed our takings and tabs information. I tried not make too much of an issue, as I didn't want to upset him.

'It's nearing a hundred euros Conner.'

'I'll speak to Patsy; she hasn't been paid for two weeks.' *Oh, so its Patsy's fault we haven't been paid, what a lame excuse* I thought. Luckily he only stayed for the one drink, which was unusual. I'd heard he and Patsy had run up a bill at another English bar several months ago; were they going to do the same with us. I hoped not as I had grown quite fond of this odd couple. One couldn't help liking Conner, once you understood him and his crooked ways which sadly ruined him. What Patsy saw in him was beyond me. She was as honest as they come. But sadly she had to swallow Conner's bad habits and dishonesty of which we were now aware.

The week soon passed. Sunday had arrived yet again, and there was no sign of Conner all week. Michael and I felt concerned, *had he done a runner?* It was Bingo and Quiz night, Patsy and Conner had become regulars for these and so had several other locals and holidaymakers. If they were going to show their faces this would be the time; if they didn't we would then know where we stood: minus a hundred euros.

I was on the phone to Michael that afternoon. We spent most our time on the telephone, it was the only time we could have a private conversation, 'Yes Jo I will ask him for the money first, no Jo I won't serve them until they pay us, I've got to go, Jo I'm busy I have 3 people waiting at the bar, goodbye.' He hung up to serve his customers. This just frustrated me, we never had time to talk, and I was stuck at home with Sarina, wondering whether Conner was going to bash Michael, once he asked him for our money. I felt nervous about the whole situation. The bar was always a worry, especially if some piss head abused me or Michael. Overall, we had managed to get rid of a lot of the bad clients to make room for the nice ones. Although we found ourselves mixing with people we normally wouldn't have, our clientele was quite varied. Seventy per cent of our customers were genuinely nice, 20 per cent had some kind of a habit: drink, drugs, con artist, bullying or bad behaviour. Leaving the odd 10 per cent who were the tight arses with attitude. As long as Michael and I had each other, then neither of us would be tempted to follow these dark paths; this was all that mattered. We both liked a drink but there was a time and place for it. We never drank whilst working behind the bar, we couldn't afford to, not when it meant dealing with people's money.

That evening Michael called me. 'Conner's been in,' he paused, 'He's paid his bill.' Relief swept through me. Michael also sounded relieved. 'Any way, I thought I'd let you know so you can stop worrying.'

'What did you say? What did he say? Did you tell him he can't have another tab?'

'No Jo, he's paid, leave it at that, I'm busy, I've got to go, oh and I'll be home late, so don't wait up.' I immediately felt hurt. I hated it when he said he'd be home late. Nevertheless I was satisfied. Conner had paid his bill. I hung up abruptly, so Michael knew I was unhappy, not that I think he cared. I sat back on the sofa, took my glass of wine and sipped it switching the telly over, to find a late movie. Sarina was already in bed asleep. I was now feeling lonely and sad, I could never sleep properly until Michael was home, and tonight was no different.

I had dozed off and woke suddenly on the sofa, the telly was buzzing and my phone had been ringing. I felt panicky; I'd missed a call, and as I'd tried to retrieve it, the phone fell to the floor. Now half awake, I reached down and grasped the phone. I recognised Michael's number, then turning my wrist to view my watch, I saw it was 3am. *What the hell is Michael doing calling me at this hour.* Suddenly the phone rang again. *I bet he can't get a taxi,* I thought, *he's obviously had too much to drink.* I answered his call abruptly, 'Yes, Michael, what is it?' There was silence and then, suddenly, a foreign voice came on the line.

'Hola, hola, hello.'

'Hello, Michael, Michael is that you? Don't mess around, Michael are you there?'

'Babe, babe it's me, I've had an accident, I'm on the scooter. I don't know where I am.' His voice was panicked and then he became tearful. Another voice came on the line, a French accent.

'He's fine, he's fallen off the scooter, Las Marinas. We are near Rio's Bar.' *Where was that?* I couldn't think as I stood up and grabbed any clothes I could reach.

'I'll be five minutes.' Michael was back on the phone.

'I've smashed my head Jo, I'm sorry, I love you.' He now sounded distressed.

'Michael, stay calm, I'm coming, you're gonna be fine. Just stand somewhere I can see you.' I rushed into Sarina's room, swept her up into my arms and carried her out to the car, struggling to lock everything as I went. It was pitch dark, with a slight chill in the air. I strapped Sarina into her car seat and covered her with a blanket. She didn't murmur, ; she was fast asleep. I eased off the drive way and down the road towards Las Marinas, a very long road, roughly ten kilometres.

I prayed, *Please God let me find him.* The road was so dark and the night seemed so long. *Where are you?,* I kept asking myself. A little ahead I saw a group of young lads, holding up my injured husband. *Shit* I thought, as I pulled the car into where they all stood. I turned the engine off, leaving the lights on as the road was in thick darkness. 'Michael!' I uttered, rushing over to hug him, he was dazed and weepy.

'Jo, I'm fine, I'm so sorry, I can't remember what happened, my ankle hurts and my head.' He became tearful. I looked at the young lads, and assessed the situation, then I looked down at Michael's ankle; it was bleeding, and a small chunk was missing. One of the lads spoke pointing towards Michael's scooter.

'We heard a crash and heard your husband call for help.' They had been out on their balcony where they were staying on vacation, enjoying beer and possibly a smoke. There were four or five of them, aged around eighteen to twenty, nice, polite and they spoke a little English. Two of them helped me get Michael into the front seat of the car. I instructed the others to take Michael's scooter off the road.

'Do you want us to take his scooter to our apartment, it's just over there?' The young lad pointed to some apartments. 'You can pick it up tomorrow, we've looked it over, and it's only scratched.'

'Please, would you and I'll take your number. Thank you so much for helping us.' I stayed in control of what was going on, checking and looking around myself, so I would recognise where to come tomorrow; I was also looking and checking for police. I was being cautious, *Had Michael been drinking?* It wasn't the time to ask, he seemed distressed and in shock. I couldn't smell booze. There were so many questions I wanted to ask but tomorrow was another day and hospital was my next port call. After thanking the lads several times, we left the scene and I took Michael home. Sarina was still fast asleep, unaware of what had taken place. I arrived home and took Michael into the house so I could see exactly what I was dealing with. He had a gash in his head and his ankle bone was exposed. 'Michael, I'm gonna get Sandra from next door. Sarina's ok, she's asleep in the car on the drive way. I'll be two secs.' Within seconds I returned back with Sandra. She took one look at Michael and said,

'Hospital, come let's go.' She volunteered her help with translating, *what would I have done without her?*

I felt nervous driving to the hospital, not feeling a hundred per cent sure where it was. Eventually I found it and pulled up outside the Emergency Department. I left the engine running and my passengers in the car, and ran straight inside the hospital. First, I acknowledged the receptionist, and then noticed a wheel chair. I walked towards it and said, *'urgencia.'* I felt panicky and upset; I felt my inner self begin to give way; tears appeared in my eyes, I choked them back. A man came out from behind his desk, half asleep; obviously the night nurse, a sturdy man dressed in his whites, plain looking, non-descript. He grabbed the chair and wheeled it towards me, spoke some Spanish which I didn't understand, and then led the way to my car. This was parked directly outside the sliding doors. I noticed no one was present in the waiting area when we passed through, which was no surprise as it was now 4am. He positioned the chair to where Michael sat, and helped him into it, then wheeled him back through the sliding doors and waited for me by the desk to take our details. *Fast, efficient service* I thought, whilst I parked the car in the car park. Sandra had followed in with Michael while I was seeing to Sarina, carefully placing her into her pushchair comfortably so she would sleep through this whole ordeal.

Once I'd returned to the desk, Michael was rapidly whisked off to x-ray. Sandra and I took a seat, a five-hour long seat. No one had come out to inform us about Michael's progress and so the five-hour wait was our punishment for not asking. Once, when we did agree to ask, we were told to return later that morning as they were waiting for a skin graft specialist, for Michael's ankle. We decided to wait on, as we'd already waited this length of time. 'I'm gonna have to call Toni, he'll be worried,' said Sandra.

'Do you want to use my phone?'

'Please.' With that I handed her my phone. My back ached, and Sarina now began to stir. It was time for her to wake up. I had nothing with me for her, no milk, water or snack. I searched my bag and came across a bottle of juice for her, thank god; I felt my panic subside. As I passed Sarina her juice, a nurse arrived to tell me my husband was now ready to return home. This was sudden; I thought we were waiting for a specialist? Sandra then returned and we all followed the nurse down the corridor to where Michael was waiting.

Michael was sitting in a wheel chair, his head was wrapped in bandage as well as his ankle.

'Babe, are you alright, I've been so worried?' I asked.

'I'm fine, they stapled my head, I mean they actually stapled me, I could hear the clunk of the staple gun.'

'Daddy, did it hurt?' piped a little voice; she had been asleep through the whole ordeal and was now awake for the best bit, the recovery.

'Hello Chucky, I'm fine, I didn't feel a thing.' Michael was now aware his daughter was on the scene. 'Are you alright? Daddy's just been a silly daddy.'

'Why are we here? When are we going home, Daddy?'

'We're going now baby girl.' Michael looked up at me and grasped my hand to assure me everything was ok.

We all returned home. I didn't open the bar that day as we were all too tired. In fact, this was the main cause of Michael's accident; he had been working 18-hour shifts and not eating properly, so as a result, he had passed out whilst riding his scooter that night. I felt the family needed to be together and appreciate what we had. Us.

* * Weddings, dogs and doctors * *

We had now recovered from Michael's scooter accident; I worked his shift as well as mine, while he convalesced. We retrieved the scooter the next day, compliments of Conner who was very supportive and checked the scooter for any damage. Michael visited the surgery every other day for nine weeks, to have the dressing cleaned and changed, until the skin grew back and covered his ankle bone. The hospital visits improved his Spanish with one of the nurses. She spoke a little English, and so they could both practice. Conner helped in taking him to the doctors, he was rewarded with beer. I now felt tired and deflated. Then one morning I received a call from a well-spoken Irish woman.

'Hello, is that Jo?' She asked.

'Yes, speaking, how can I help you?'

'Hi I saw your advert in the Female Focus, you specialise in Wedding hair?'

'Yes, I do.' So the conversation led off from there. We made arrangements to meet at the Marriot Hotel. At first I thought there was some kind of a con behind the arrangement. Nevertheless I still went along to the interview as the prospect of working in luxury hotels and dressing bridal hair certainly appealed to me.

I met the Irish woman in the bar lounge of the hotel. We recognised one another as if we had already met before. 'Hello, I'm Marcella, you must be Jo.' Did I look like an obvious hairdresser? Or did I just look lost? Maybe both.

'Hi, yes I'm Jo.' I didn't voice Marcella's name as I was worried I couldn't pronounce it.

'Come over, I've just ordered coffee, what would you like?' Marcella asked, leading me over to the cosy lounge area of the Marriot. This was me, in a luxury 5 star hotel. The lounge area was large and spacious, perfectly situated between the bar and reception, a perfect place to sit and people-watch all day. The lounge also looked outside onto a patio area, displaying several large figurines and steps, which led down to the swimming pool. Everything, pretty much was visible from the lounge, including views of their fabulous 18-hole golf course.

'Coffee's great for me.' We both sat down.

'How long have you lived here Jo?' Marcella asked, whilst I was still nosing around.

'Um, only this year.' *Was that a good answer, should I have lied, and said two or three years, maybe?* I thought, but it was too late. I hoped she didn't think I was a fly by night, like a lot of the expats. I then informed her that we had bought here, so she knew that we intended to stay long term. Marcella is a wedding planner, here in Spain, and most of her clients come over from Ireland. Because of its Catholicism, Spain offers beautiful, historic Catholic churches, along with plenty of sunshine, and reasonably-priced holidays for those who want to share quality time together. She also arranges blessing. (Blessings are in lieu of a wedding celebration for couples who may have differences in religion or who may already be married, or for any other reason, who still may want to celebrate) So, here she was looking for a professional hairdresser who could put hair up. The meeting went very well and gave me the boost that I needed at that time; I was missing my hairdressing trade and to be offered wedding-hair work was music to my ears. We arranged to meet in the spring of the following year. Marcella is a strong business woman and knows her own mind; she's an elegantly dressed lady who doesn't suffer fools gladly; I liked her instantly because of her professionalism.

I left the meeting full of excitement and ambition, only to then return back to the bar. Michael was there, covering for me. He was sat at the bar having a coffee with Jenny, Conner was also there, drinking his usual tankard of beer. They were all in deep conversation until I entered. 'So how did you get on, was it a waste of time?' Michael asked inquisitively.

'Actually no. The meeting went very well. Marcella is a wedding planner and she organises weddings and blessings in 5-star hotels, all based along the Costa

Blanca. And she wants me to join her team doing the hair.'

'Well done, babe. When do you start?' He said, vaguely.

'Next Spring, it's only during the summer season.' I replied. I could sense what Michael was thinking, by his questions. 'Don't panic it's only part-time, possibly 2 or 3 times a week. I can make arrangements for someone to cover my shift in the bar.'

'Well done Jo,' Jenny murmured, her bar stool made a screeching sound as she stood up from where she had been drinking her coffee, stubbing out the last remains of her cigarette into the ashtray. She then went over to the sink behind the bar to wash her hands.

'Right, I'd better go and get Sarina. Conner, another beer? Jo will serve you.' Oh well, that was enough about me, back to the grindstone. Michael then left to fetch our daughter issuing his orders as he went. Sarina was settled in school and finished at five. It was a long day for a 3 year-old; they had a long lunch break, for which Sarina stayed. She started school at 9 o'clock, so by the time we picked her up she would often be asleep in the car before we got home or back to the bar. As we didn't have a regular babysitter, her school hours helped give Michael and me the time to work and organise ourselves. Then the thought crossed my mind, *Shit, what about Sarina? What will I do with her during the summer? She's on her school holidays from the end of June to the beginning of September. I won't be able to take her with me to these weddings, my god she'd scare the brides out of wed lock and childbirth. I'm sure I'll think of something; Michael will just have to take her to work with him.* I had a few months to organise this but first there was Christmas to worry about. *Was Louis going to join us? Do we close the bar Christmas day?*

Annette then entered the bar with her dog, Gomish, and this broke my thoughts. 'Hello Jo, anyone cooking?' she asked dragging out a bar stool from the bar, a sound that I had become familiar with.

'Yes, I am,' Jenny answered tying her apron on.

'Perfect, a glass of wine first and a burger. Jo are you joining me?' By now her dog had plonked himself down beneath her feet on the cold, tiled flooring, instantly dosing off as he knew the routine, until the smell of food arrived and then he was on red alert. Annette did like her afternoon sessions and was very generous as a Dutch woman.

'Yes, why not, I deserve a glass of wine.'

'You do?'

'Yes I do.' I pulled up a stool next to her and explained about the meeting I'd had with the wedding planner. Jenny poured our wines before leaving to cook the burger. Annette always seemed interested in what I had to say, more than I could say about Michael. She was a sympathetic listener. Conner finished his beer in a couple of gulps; he'd already heard this story once and that was enough for him, so he left. Once again, he left his bill unpaid but he was good for it. This now left only me, Annette and her hound in the bar, as business had now slowed down after our first summer season. We would now need to depend on our expat community to see us through the winter months. Despite having managed to save some money, sadly this was taken from our bank account to pay one year's non-payment of social security plus fines and interest. Our German accountant had not set the direct debit up correctly, nor had he given our correct address, so we didn't receive any bills from the tax office. We learnt the hard way and kept a check on our Spanish bank statements. Ignorance, as well as badly appointed accountants, can cost you in Spain.

'Annette, what happens here at Christmas?' I enquired.

'Nothing, most people return back to their own countries to be with their families. The Spanish don't really celebrate it as much as the English, Dutch and German. They celebrate The Three Kings, that's the 6th January. They believe the Three Kings brought the gifts,' Annette explained.

'So, do they decorate their homes?' I asked.

'Not like we do back home, a little.'

'What about the shops?' Not really, a little bit, Jo you just have to wait, you'll see.' Michael had now returned with Sarina, who ran up the few steps outside and into the bar, until she saw Gomish and stopped in her tracks.

She was nervous around him, not that he would hurt her, but he was a big dog that drooled. Michael then entered, grasping Sarina's hand to reassure her. They both strolled over to join Annette and me. Michael and Sarina stood nervously staring down at Gomish, and Gomish lifted up an eyelid to see who had disturbed him from his sleep. Not taking any interest and recognising the company, he then returned back to his doze.

'Will you two stop staring at that dog; it unnerves a dog if you stare it straight in the face,' I insisted. Annette took no notice of their fear. As far as she was concerned, they had the problem not her Gomish; she knew he was safe, she had trained him to walk off lead and to obey, which he did. Michael was nervous of all dogs, he had been bitten by a Chihuahua when he was a small boy and had has been scared ever since, so this fear now had rubbed off onto Sarina. After a while in Gomish's company, Sarina always managed a few sneaky strokes.

'Daddy, I'm hungry,' Sarina groaned, whilst we were all discussing what to do in the bar over Christmas. Michael went off to fetch her some sausages, which had been cooked earlier that day and refrigerated for the next day's breakfasts. Jenny had left; she finished her shift after cooking Annette's burger. He now returned with two sausages, gave Sarina one to hold so she could nibble on it as and when she preferred, and the other one, naturally, Gomish got, which he lapped up in seconds; he always got something from the kitchen but never went into it, he would always wait. Even if Annette entered the kitchen, he was always told to wait, which he did that day. I wanted to show Annette our new chip fryer leaving Michael, Sarina and Gomish together in the bar.

'How much did you pay?' Annette queried, 'I think you were robbed.'

'No, Annette, it's a professional one and stainless steel, we had to buy it, the one that came with the bar broke, like everything else that came with the bar.' Now Michael had entered the kitchen and joined the conversation.

'It'll last forever, Annette.' Annette still wasn't convinced by the price.

'I know that Michael, but six hundred and forty euros, it should be gold.' We were all laughing at Annette's comment, when suddenly we heard Sarina scream, *Shit, the dog!*

We all rushed out of the kitchen, Sarina was lying on the floor, crying next to Gomish. Michael swept her up into his arms to see what the matter was. 'Sarina, what happened?'

'Gomish bit me.' she mumbled out, with floods of tears. We all looked down at Gomish, he looked puzzled. Annette was certain Gomish wouldn't have done such a thing.

'Gomish? No Sarina, were you teasing him?' Annette asked now taking Gomish to her side.

'No, I fell and he took my sausage.' Sarina yelled

with tears streaming down her cheeks together with chewed-up sausage and dribble falling from her mouth. I looked closely and he had nipped her slightly on her cheek. My god, we had left them only for a short time and look at what had happened - he could have taken off half her face.

'Jo, look Gomish wouldn't bite her intentionally, he was obviously after her sausage and missed and caught her cheek, and it was an accident.' Annette kept repeating. 'Also she fell on the dog.'

'Michael, you shouldn't have left her.' I said accusingly.

'Jo, I'm sorry, it was for 2 seconds, they were fine when I left them, look it's just a little scratch, calm down.' But, I couldn't, I kept thinking about what could have happened.

'Mummy, I want to go home.'

'Yes, baby, come on let's go.' I took Sarina into my arms and left the bar. Michael and Annette were still pondering about what had just taken place.

I strapped Sarina into her car seat and took another glance at her cheek: yes it was a little scratch, he'd obviously just caught her with one of his canines, but what about rabies?

Without any hesitation, I took her straight to our local village doctor. Sarina had calmed down by the time we entered the reception area of the surgery. I had all my words planned in my head and how I was to pronounce them. 'Is possible to have a doctor? My daughter was bitten by my friend's dog.' That was all I said. Well, Sarina and I were seen to straight away, emergency alert; a Doctor was called urgently, all sorts of questions were then thrown at me. Whose was the dog? Did we know the dog? A form from the police would have to be filled out with all the dog's details. While this was going on, the doctor had arrived and more questions were now being asked about Sarina, all in Spanish. I became panicked, I didn't know whom to answer first and I didn't understand half their questions. Suddenly the nice nurse arrived, with relief I recognised her straight away, she had dressed Michael's ankle for him after his scooter accident. She spoke a little English, which helped reassure me. She explained that Sarina would have two injections in her bottom, Tetanus and Rabies. My poor Sarina, I didn't expect all this fuss, I only wanted to ask a doctor to take a look. Dog bites are taken very seriously here in Spain and, as far as the Doctor was concerned: treat the patient and then treat the dog.

'Perdon, no entiendo.' (Sorry I don't understand) I couldn't give out information on the dog, this was my friend's best friend, and it was an accident. Shoot the dog; oh no I couldn't be responsible for that. My story changed, I didn't know the dog, and it had run off, and I couldn't understand any more Spanish, which was a good excuse. I left the surgery exhausted. Sarina was still in shock; she had screamed the surgery down especially

when they injected her behind. I called Michael, 'Michael, I want to go back to England.' Then I sobbed and explained the whole ordeal.

* * *Christmas in Spain* * *

It was now only a few days before Christmas. The weather had changed; all the Spanish parents at school were in their coats, whilst we British were still in our t-shirts. *'Muy frio.'* they would say to me, this meant very cold. 'No.' I would reply; England is cold, this weather was similar to our English spring/summer time, when the sun shone. Here, in Spain the sun shines nearly every day, it is warmer outside in the sun than inside at this time of year, November to April. The Spanish homes are built to keep the sun out, so heating them is difficult, especially the newer properties; there is little or no insulation and damp is also a problem.

Louis had arrived into sunshine; he had left the rain showers of Essex, England, early that morning. The next few days were already planned: first there was *'Papa Noel'* (Santa Claus). Sarina was excited to show off her older brother to her friends. Louis wasn't so keen. 'Do I have to go mum, can't I stay here?'

'No, Louis, I have to go and I want you to see Sarina and her new school.'

'Dad's not going.'

'I know, he has to work, that's why I need you to go, please Louis,' I begged. I was also excited to show Louis Sarina's new school, *Papa Noel* and her school concert about which I had yet to inform him. I thought I'd break that one gently. It was great having Louis home for Christmas; we had decided to have a Christmas Eve party in the bar with live music and close on the Christmas day. I had arranged for my friend to bring her son and his mate, so Louis had someone his own age here. There would be seventeen at the party. Jane and Cole were also coming with Hayley, so that would keep Sarina entertained; I had become good friends with Jane since meeting her at Paul's BBQ. The girls had also become friends and got on most of the time.

I had already taken Sarina to school earlier that morning. At first ,she didn't want to go, she wanted to wait for her brother's arrival. But I reminded her of *Papa Noel* and that she would see Louis later, at the same time, so she settled for this.

We arrived at The Casa De La Cultura (Community Centre). This is a large building based in the middle of Els Poblets; it overlooks the main road which passes through the village. We took the stairs leading us up onto a large balcony; we then followed the other mothers into the hall. It was cold as we entered. *Papa Noel* had his seat on the stage in front of us, he awaited his destiny patiently, checking that his sack was complete and in place for the rush and anticipation of children. Lots of parents had already arrived and gathered into their circles for gossip. I joined the group reluctantly; I was never one to mix with the Mummy society, but as a foreigner I felt I should make the effort and this would help improve my Spanish. I introduced Louis to them, a couple of them looked surprised that I should have a son of his age and waited for an explanation. I couldn't explain how I had come to be a young mum, so I left them to make their own judgements.

Louis looked around for his sister, he was already bored. The children began to arrive, all holding hands, single file as they entered with their teacher. Sarina's class was first as they were the youngest. Sarina instantly spotted her brother; she wanted to run over and hug him but was distracted by this man on stage with his white imitation beard and red and white silk cloth as his costume. Then I noticed her attention change over to his sack that was full to the top with pressies. She glanced over at us and gave a rather large smile, then turned to her friends to discuss her brother and Santa. The gifts were given to each child whilst they sat upon Santa's knee and placed their orders for Christmas. A photo was also taken and placed into a decorated card that had been made previously by the particular child. Once this episode was over, the children were able to join their parents. Sarina charged over and flung her arms around her brother. He hugged her, then held her back and asked, 'What did Santa give you?'

'*Chuches.*' She replied. 'Sweets.' Sarina held out a plastic coned-shape bag full of an assortment of sweets. 'Do you want one, Lou, Lou?'

'No, you keep them.'

'Have you got me a pressie for Christmas?'

'I might 'ave. Have you been a good girl?' Louis asked, knowing her answer.

'Yes, haven't I Mummy?'

'Yes Sarina.' I glanced over at her teacher and noticed her calling the children back. 'Come on Sarina, your teacher's calling you, you'll see Louis later, come on babe, off you go.' She left us reluctantly, but once she joined her friends she was full of herself and waved us goodbye as her class left the building, holding hands, following their teacher back to school.

'So now where Mum?' Louis asked.

'Shall we visit Dad in the bar? As he was out early picking you up from the airport.' Michael dropped Louis off to me earlier that morning, he wanted to see the Papa Noel visit but he had to return to work for a delivery of beer. There was only 2 days to go before Christmas, so there was lots to organise.

'Ok, we can have breakfast.' Louis suggested. We left on that idea.

Michael was pleased to see us; the bar was empty. Business had really slowed down now that we were in the winter months; it was like a ghost town. 'Alright Lou, how was Santa?' Michael asked as we entered the bar.

'Alright, are you gonna cook us brekkie?'

'Yeah, do you want one Mum?' Michael asked leaving the screeching stool beneath him.

'No, thanks, I've eaten, I'll have a coffee though.'

'Sorry Lou, I had to rush off this morning.'

'No problem. Dad, are you working tonight?' Louis had called Michael *dad* since our wedding day. Michael had been thrilled when Louis had asked him on the day.

'Yes son, why don't you, Mum and Sarina come down for a drink this evening? Sarina hasn't got school tomorrow.'

'Michael, you're forgetting its Sarina's school Christmas concert tonight.' I reminded him and then realised I hadn't mentioned this to Louis.

'What's that Mum?' He asked.

'Oh yeah, Lou, its Sarina's concert, its back at The Casa De Cultura, where we were this morning It starts at eight.'

'Mum, can't I stay with Dad?' I looked angrily at Michael. I wasn't that keen on going myself, especially without Michael and Louis.

'Lou, it won't be on that long and Dad's working, you'll be bored here, and Sarina's expecting you.'

'Yeah Lou, go with your mother, keep her company, son.' Louis agreed, much to his annoyance. Then the 'Looky Looky' man strolled into the bar with his rugs thrown over his shoulder. 'Hey, Lionel Richie.' Michael chorused as Lionel approached us.

'Hola, Hola, que tale?' (How are you)? He asked,

'Bien, bien.' (Good) was always the polite answer. Michael had re-named Jave Bee to Lionel Richie several years ago now, so everyone called him Lionel, and yes, he was the spitting image of the singer, Lionel Richie. Lionel was from Morocco and worked as a 'Looky, looky' man in Denia, selling the usual wares that they sell. It must be pretty lucrative as it supports his three wives who live in Morocco. He tells us that he could have up to 4 wives but he only has a 3-floor property, with a wife living on each floor. He once asked Michael, how many wives did he have? As mentioned before, Michael replied four, in the past tense. Lionel only understood the present so he was most impressed with Michael. He didn't stay too long; I no longer had the money to buy rugs or tablecloths, as I had in the past.

We enjoyed our breakfast time together; Louis ate while we drank coffee and discussed our plans for Christmas. I noticed a small change in Louis, it had only been 3 months since I'd last seen him, and he seemed to have no patience with me. Perhaps he'd always been like this and by having time apart, it was only now that I noticed and this was something I would have to live with.

The Casa De Cultura was packed. We arrived a little late. Sarina ran off to join her classmates; she was dressed as a bumble bee. Louis and I took stood alongside other parents who were also too late for seats. Jane then joined us and remarked, 'Oh, you were late like me.'

'Yes, how you doing?' I asked.

'Fine, until I got here. They look as if they've brought their neighbours as well as the whole family.' Both Jane and I looked around us; it was packed tight, not an empty seat to be had. We were squashed in like sardines, god help us if there was a fire, no health and safety requirements were upheld here.

'Where's Cole?' I asked.

'He's home, he wouldn't come to anything like this Jo, he doesn't like crowds.' Nor did I. I just took lots of deep breaths and concentrated on something else, such as the Fire Exit.

'Jane, this is my son, Louis.' I introduced them both and was then silenced by a young girl on a microphone, repeating herself several times, *'Silencio, silencio Por favor.'* No one took any notice; all we could hear was a competitive humming of chatter and this girl repeating herself; it was unorganised, it was chaos. Eventually, the audience acknowledged this poor girl's plea and slowly droned their chatter to a silence. Louis and I looked at each other, alarmed by the whole experience; we shared our alarm with Jane, our faces said it all! The three of us thought we were going to watch a nativity play. But no, we experienced pop music, mainly Michael Jackson, on a sound system that crackled with old age and competing with a rather noisy audience.

Sarina and her little tribe of classmates were all dressed like bumble bees, and sang, 'ding, dong, da,' otherwise known as *Jingle Bells*. It was lovely listening to carol music in Spanish, I was so proud.

The concert went on longer than I had anticipated; we left at 10 o'clock. Louis was tired, he'd had a long day, and travelling the early hours that morning, from England to Spain, had now caught up with him. Sarina was buzzing. 'Is it Christmas, is it Christmas now Mummy?' She asked as we left the Cultura.

'No darling, Christmas eve is tomorrow, then its Christmas.' We decided to call it a day, and return home. We took a rain cheque on Michael's offer for a drink. The concert had been videoed, so Michael wasn't too disappointed, especially once I informed him of the whole experience. Sarina had enjoyed it, she didn't know any different.

Louis and Sarina were up early the next day. They woke me for breakfast. 'It doesn't feel like Christmas.' Louis remarked, sadly.

'I've put up decorations Lou, what do you mean?'

'Well. your house and next door are the only ones decorated in the whole street.'

'That's because we're the only resident people who live here all year, the rest of the properties are holiday homes.' I answered climbing out of bed.

'Yeah, but what about the shops? I've only noticed a few decorated.' He was right, Christmas was celebrated here, but not on a large scale like England; with competitively decorated houses, shops and streets. The

Spanish didn't have carol singers either. There were only a few lights in the sparsely decorated the villages and the odd Christmas tree. Every year I'm told that the decorations are an improvement from the previous Christmas.

Essentially, the Spanish celebrate *The Three Kings* which is held on the 6th January. They believe the Kings brought the gifts, not Santa. All the same, gifts and celebration still took place in Spanish households on Christmas day.

On the eve of the 5th January, Denia holds a carnival procession; floats holding the Three Kings who leave from the Port and head towards the Marques De campo, passing around the streets of Denia, throwing large amounts of sweets at the onlookers. Many floats participate in this fiesta, which are decorated in silks and gems to transport the several different Three Kings. Horses, camels, donkeys and lamas also feature at this event. The floats are usually led by a man in costume who bashes a rather large base drum and is followed by a procession of marching bands. The streets of Denia are alive and busy on this occasion.

Now it was quiet all round Denia; most of the expats had left to visit their families for Christmas, leaving only a few of us here. This was why we had decided to have a Christmas Eve party, full of music and dancing at the bar, not forgetting Santa Claus, Michael in disguise.

Christmas Eve soon came round; the bar was busy

with its regulars and visitors. We started the evening off with song sheets and everyone joined in singing the Christmas carols, also singing along with our live music act, Jake, a good looking solo artist with a mop of hair. He had recently shed 4 stone in weight and now attracted unwanted admirers. He also played the guitar, not very well, I might add, but this made the evening. Michael was armed with several cds to play after his performance.

Sarina was dressed as a fairy and ran around full of excitement and out of control. I was busy in the kitchen scraping burnt sausage rolls off a baking tray, satisfied that they were only burnt underneath, and would go unnoticed until eaten. Louis sat at the bar with Sean and Rob. Both lads were the same age as Louis, unemployed but seeking a future of work in Spain. They had both attended Spanish school and spoke the *Castellano* language very well. To attend Valencia University , one had to also speak *Valenciano*, the local dialect Franco had once forbidden when he was in power. This was why I chose Sarina's school, so she spoke both fluently. Sadly, the boys only spoke *Castellano*, so education and work for them was very limited. Louis mixed well with the lads. I had met Rob's mum only recently; she was a good customer of ours, a striking woman, blonde, slim but a piss head. She was a Londoner who often used the F word quite loosely, although not inoffensively; a bubbly woman who loved to gossip and that was fine as long as you weren't the subject.

I noticed Colin arrive with Sharon, *Surely he wasn't her latest victim? normally she went for young boys.* I thought. 'Did I just see Colin come in with Sharon?' Jenny asked whilst wiping a glass.

'Yes, he must be desperate.' replied Lyn, who was also working on that night, her husband being away for Christmas on a rig somewhere. He was due back Boxing Day, so Lyn offered her services for bar duty. She always had a lot of fun behind the bar and was popular with the punters. Jenny was helping out for only a couple of hours; she had other arrangements with her friends. Both the girls wore tinsel around their necks; I had taken mine off as it had nearly caught on fire whilst I was attempting to cook.

'Hi Sharon, what are you drinking?' I asked staring towards Colin. 'Colin, what about you, what do you want to drink? Oh and whose bill shall I put this on?' How nosey was I?

'Separate, please Jo.' Colin answered. *Ah, I have my answer; it was sex, not a relationship. Thank god, Colin was far too good for this aggressive man eater.* Sharon fluttered her eye lashes towards Colin and then replied sweetly,

'A glass of wine Jo.' My god she must have had her oats, was she the same woman or was it Christmas? The car sales man then arrived to join Sharon and Colin.

'A *caña*, please Jo, where's Michael?' he asked, still bathing himself in *Kouros*, the smell intoxicated me.

'He's down the road somewhere, dressed as Santa and ringing a bell, he should be here in 5 minutes.'

'Santa?'

'Yes, Sharon, it's Christmas, kids love Santa. If you're lucky you might get a chance to sit on his knee.' I said and waited for a critical answer back, but instead she smiled and gave the idea a thought; sick. The bar got busier as the evening went on. I noticed Conner and Patsy weren't here, which was strange; Conner had said they were coming, but that was a few days ago, he hadn't been in since.

Santa then arrived, his costume looked tight (it was the last one in the shop as I couldn't find his regular one, it had got lost during the move). Sarina's eyes nearly popped out of her head, she pushed her way through the small crowd of children and took her place on Santa's knee and then examined Santa. 'My Daddy's got a ring like that.' as she questioned Michael, he distracted her to his sack of gifts, which worked for a while. She watched each child sit on Santa's knee to see if they had a better toy than her, then pointed to Santa's wedding ring and whispered to Hayley, 'Santa has the same ring as my Daddy.' I heard her say this while collecting glasses. Then, much to my annoyance, Sharon was on Santa's knee, laughing and giggling. Michael looked quite nervous, she was tipsy and having fun. With all the gifts now distributed, Sarina ran off with her friend. Both the girls behind the bar looked directly at me and then at Michael, scrutinising the obvious.

'She's just having fun girls.' I said returning with a handful of empty glasses. Michael wasn't, he stood up, half pushing Sharon off his knee and made a fast exit to the kitchen, so he could change.

Sharon returned to the bar, stumbling on route. 'Cocktail Jo, I'll have a cocktail, anyone, you decide, surprise me.' The only one I knew was a screaming orgasm, which by all accounts, she looked like she'd already had one.

Colin was now dismissive of her behaviour and stood the other side of the bar with the car salesman and his wife.

Louis looked like he was having fun. I then noticed Rob's mum arrive alone. She too looked a little worse for wear, so I decided to join them. 'Where's Richard, Lydia?' Richard was a DIY man; this wasn't his profession, but an excuse to get out of the house for obvious reasons. I don't think he needed to work for money; he'd owned a very successful business in the UK and had sold it for a small fortune.

'He's fucked off home as usual, say's I'm pissed. It's fucking Christmas, course I'm pissed.' Well there was no arguing with that. Then I noticed Louis looking tipsy.

'Louis, have you been drinking?'

'Yeah, we're having shots, you want one?' he slurred.

'I'll have one.' Lydia urged clambering onto a

barstool. Five *Anis Tenis* were then ordered, 48 per cent alcohol, which crystalizes when kept in the freezer. Each of us took our shots and knocked them back.

'No more Louis, stick to shandy now.'

'Alright, Mother. But Lydia says it's effing Christmas.'

'Louis, watch your tongue.' I said sternly and left on that note to join Colin for a drink. Lydia followed shortly after.

'Alright Jo, are you having a good time?' he asked.

'Yes, I think so.' I then waved over at Paul and Ally; they were sitting at the opposite end of the bar. Alex was in deep conversation with someone, Shelley was knocking back the Malibu, much to Paul's disgust, as he had to pick up the bill. Lydia had now joined us, stumbling on route.

'So why is a fucking good looking man like you single?' Lydia spluttered, nearly falling on Colin and me. How embarrassing, Colin didn't care for bad language. But I awaited the answer.

'Who says I'm single?' Colin answered dryly. The conversation ended there. Lydia got the message and staggered back to the boys. I also followed her to check she got there in one piece. She was wrecked, her face was rosy and her eyes were blinking blood shot, with smudged mascara.

'He's fucking gay, if you ask me.' She muttered under her breath; she was now propped up by the bar.

'Do you want me to call you a taxi?' I asked, hoping the answer was going to be yes.

'Yeah, Rob we're going. I'm pissed.' One was called straight away, before she passed out.

Michael was back behind the bar, he was happier there than in costume until Jenny whispered something in his ear. He marched out from the bar area, armed with a mop and bucket and headed towards the toilets.

'Everything ok babe?' I asked as he passed me.

'No, some bastard has pissed on the floor in the ladies.'

I made no comment, this job was best his. He soon returned behind the bar. Jenny had now finished her shift and left, wishing us all a merry Christmas.

Michael still looked grumpy. 'What's the matter, have you got the hump because Jenny's left?'

'No, I'm pissed off, mopping up piss, sick and shit.'

'Has someone been sick?' I asked, trying to keep a smile on my face behind the bar.

'No, but someone's left their thong on the toilet floor, so I binned it.'

Oh, my god, I thought, *someone has lost their knickers.* 'What if they go back for them?'

'Fuck 'em.' he said, and then walked off to serve someone, leaving me standing in shock, *How humiliating, fancy losing your knickers!*

'Mummy, I'm tired, can we go now?' Sarina, was

shattered, sweat was running through her fine tousled hair, she had lost her wings and juice was down the front of her dress.

'Yes darling, let's call a taxi and get Louis.' This was a good time to leave, Louis was pissed, and Michael was pissed off, as for Sarina and me? We were both worn out. We left as did Paul who had Shelley over his shoulder, fireman style, due to too much Malibu consumption. Alex and Ally followed behind. 'Mmmmerry Christmas,' Alex shouted, cheerfully.

'You too.' I replied, guiding Sarina and Louis into a taxi.

Apart from Christmas Eve, it had been a quiet time, just Michael and me with the kids Christmas day. Not one of my best Christmases, But then when are they ever?

As for the thong! We never found out who belonged to it. Michael had mentioned a woman who had sat at the bar with her knees not too close together, but he never mentioned who it she was.

Also, we never saw Patsy and Conner again; they had mysteriously left that Christmas. Gossip was that Conner was on the run. We never knew the truth, sadly I missed this odd couple.

* * *Fiesta time and the* Fallas * *

Usually it rains during the month of the *Fallas*, but in 2006 we had brilliant sunshine. Paper Mache statues were assembled all around Denia, naughty cartoon characters displaying a little piece of nudity or just baring all. Immaculately designed and sculptured in all sizes by the different local communities. There are over 350 *Fallas* communities in and around Valencia.

Originally the *Fallas* Festival represented the coming of spring. In earlier times the statues were piles of winter junk that got burnt to make space in the houses signifying getting rid of the old and welcoming the new.

Fallas tents were pitched up near to their statues sculptures, so members of the *Fallas* community could socialise during the fiesta. In my opinion it is an excuse for them to party all week. The *Fallas Festival* is about keeping the community spirit together. Yes one big piss up!

This is one of the most spectacular fiestas in Denia. For a full week there is some activity on going: from constructing statues, marching bands and girls in their *Fallera* costumes, no expense being spared. These gowns are a costly affair, made of brocade and lace; they can cost parents anything from 1,200 up to 6,000 euros for pure silk. The gown comes as a skirt and bodice and each dress is tailor-made with shoes to match the bodice. The women's hair is parted in the centre, with a plaited, woven bun hair piece attached to either side of their head, which is then twisted in circles; three golden combs finish the look along with a necklace and large Spanish-styled earrings. Each day the women parade the streets along with the *Falleros* who are also in traditional costume. The offering of the flowers is always the busiest celebration; this is a ritual whereby each *Fallera* has flowers to take and place by the church to be presented to the Virgin Mary. 'Mummy, can I dress up in one of those costumes?' Sarina asked as we pushed her in her pushchair through the crowds of Denia.

'We'll see, I hear they're very expensive. Over there Michael, look, Paul and Ally are by that bar on the corner.'

'We must be mad coming out at 11 o'clock at night to see a load of statues burn.'

'Come on, stop moaning.' I urged, also feeling tired myself.

'You found us, then.' Paul welcomed me with the usual Spanish kiss on each cheek, along with the unpleasant smell of tobacco.

'Yeah, just about, it's packed. I've never seen Denia so busy. When do they start the burning?' I asked.

177

'Hi Jo, 12 o'clock.' Ally replied, also welcoming us with the traditional Spanish cheek-to-cheek kiss. 'They start with the childrens' statues at the bottom of the street, then work their way round, that's after they've all been judged.' With that I noticed the fire brigade arrive near to the statue where we were standing. 'This one's next, then we walk round to the next one which is only on the opposite street, over there.' Ally pointed at with her plastic cup of wine. Michael had gone to get a beer and soon returned with our drinks.

'Sorry luv, only plastic cups.' My face dropped with disappointment, drinking wine from a plastic cup, did nothing for me, I'd rather had gone without the wine.

The statue in front of me was huge, a sea horse which reached to the top of the buildings in front of me, giving me neck-ache as I looked up. The statue was then lit and it burned like a towering inferno; the fire brigade had their hoses aimed and jetted water onto the neighbouring properties to protect them from the burning. As for we civilians, there was no health and safety guideline – we had only to get out of the way as the statue burnt and fell to the ground. I thought *This is crazy, what a waste of time and money building something all year to then burn as a result.* By now Sarina had fallen asleep in her pushchair; she had missed the burning blaze which was probably for the best, she would only have asked loads of questions. 'Jo, move back.' Michael shouted and grabbed my arm, pulling me backwards as well as dragging Sarina's pushchair back with us. A large piece of the statue fell just by where we were standing.

'Oh my god, that could have landed on us.' I stressed in shock.

'Shall we move on to the next one?' Paul suggested rather quickly, trying to take my mind off the current climax that had just occurred. We did so, but after seeing one statue burn, what was the point of seeing another and I hadn't quite got over the burning statue incident nearly landing on us. I had enjoyed visiting the statues during the day in the sunshine, taking photos - this was the safer option. They were all truly magnificent, works of art. We managed to lose Ally and Paul in the crowds; this wasn't such a bad thing. Paul was very enthusiastic about the whole burning of the statues; after watching several of them burn to piles of ash, enough was enough. I was glad I'd gone; once seen never forgotten. Safety wasn't a major issue; common sense played a major part.

We left the crowd of people partying and the noise of firecrackers behind us as we walked towards our car, peace and darkness surrounded us. It was the end of yet another fiesta.

* * *Another fiesta* – San Juan * *

Another year had quickly passed. More expats were selling up and returning to England. The credit crisis was upon us. We noticed more of our regulars leave and our holiday trade slow down. Michael and I decided this would be our last summer in the bar. This was the year to sell, find a hairdressing salon in Denia.

I was finishing my shift in the bar with Lyn waitressing at my side. We were waiting for Michael to arrive and take over from our shift; he had been at the wholesalers. Instead, Pat entered with two of his friends ordering two beers and a breakfast: 'I'll have an English breakfast and a perm.' Pat was a retired doorman from Blackpool. He was a large strapping man with a bubbly personality whom you didn't want to get on the wrong side of. A man you couldn't age, he was in his sixties but he behaved like a man in his, forties, living life full to the brim, drinking and over-exerting himself with women.

'A perm?' I queried.

'Yes, you're a hairdresser aren't you? When can you do it?' he asked furtively, looking over his shoulder towards the other lads. He obviously didn't want them to hear his conversation about wanting a perm. 'I just want a body perm, no curl.' he said running his fingers through his hair. I noticed his knuckles were out of shape; they had been broken at some stage in his life. I wasn't familiar with this man, I had only served him a couple of times and heard some dodgy stories about him, but he was serious about having a perm, *So what the hell, its money,* I thought.

'Tomorrow, I can do your hair at 3 o'clock, where do you live?'

'Dead opposite, the house with the blue gate.' He left his phone number and returned to his mates who were now comfortably sat in the sun on our terrace.

Michael then arrived with a large box in his arms, filled with spirit, 'Afternoon.' he said, 'there's more in the car Jo, give us a hand.' I nodded and went out to fetch the rest of the stock; there were only two more boxes to bring in. Michael followed me out to the car, to help with the last box.

'Pat wants me to perm his hair tomorrow.' I said hoisting a large box of spirit out of the car; Michael frowned.

'You're not serious, you don't know this man, they say he's a gangster.' He slammed the boot to the car with a thud. He was obviously upset with me, but no, he wasn't jealous!

'Yes, well this gangster wants a perm.' I replied angrily.

'He's taking the piss.'

'No, his quite serious, so don't mention it to him in front of his mates.' I lowered the tone.

'Jo, you're not going, he probably fancies you.' Pat did have a reputation with the ladies.

'I've already said I'm going, I can't let him down.'

I didn't let him down. I arrived at the stated time and place. Pat had just washed his hair; he welcomed me with a glass of wine and showed me around his property, this was the usual ex-pat thing to do.

'I used to be a barber.' he said. I I was rolling his hair with large perm rods. 'It was when I spent a little time inside.' he went on. *Oh great!* I thought, *maybe Michael had been right about him.* But he told me this humorous story of how he pretended to be a barber and used to shave all the inmates' hair, so he could skive off the menial jobs. I now acknowledged Pat as being a *right character,* But harmless? I wasn't sure. He was a gentlemen; around me. Pat had himself a body perm and I had found myself a new best friend. Much to Michael's dismay, having his wife hang around with a retired, womanising ex-con wasn't to his liking. Soon enough Pat became good friends with both of us and a regular punter of the bar. He had filled Conner's shoes.

Michael also, met himself a good friend, at the beginning of that same summer. He had been busy working behind the bar all night. The usual crowd were in: James the magician, the car salesman, Sharon the man eater, Paul, Ally and co., several Spanish regulars and some holiday makers. It was two in the morning, Michael was feeling tired and the car salesman was taking over as usual, ordering Michael around as if he owned the bar. Then in walked Dinie and two Spanish women. Michael strolled over to them as they walked up the steps to our bar and said, 'Sorry were closed.'

They looked over at the crowded bar and said, 'But you have people here drinking.' to which Michael replied quite harshly, 'I'm closing.' The car salesman then stepped in and whispered in Michael's ear, 'Do you know who that is? She owns one of the busiest bars in Denia.' Michael whispered back, 'I don't give a shit, I'm tired and I'm locking up.' This agitated Michael all the more; the car salesman thought he was in control of Michael, but not on this occasion. The women left and swore never to drink in our bar ever again.

Michael awoke the next day and explained to me what had happened. He was now feeling guilty about his actions from the previous night and decided to go for a drink at this Spanish woman's bar to apologise. He took Annette and her dog with him for support - Annette went most places with Michael during the day, especially if it involved alcohol. They were like two kids when they were together. Annette found the story amusing when Michael had asked her to join him; she knew the Spanish bar and its owner, Juanita. They stayed for the afternoon; I took care of the bar. It was the longest apology I'd ever heard of. Michael was properly introduced to all three of the women whom he had thrown out of the bar, the previous night. Dinie was a Dutch, attractive woman in her fifties and I suspect, well groomed and educated. She and her husband are accountants with their own practice in Holland. She was here on vacation for 3 months, and as always, alone for the first month, after which her family joined her. The other two women were sisters, one was Juanita who owned the bar in which they were drinking and the other was Pilar, who worked part-time for her sister. All three women forgave Michael and found him rather amusing. Unlike myself, waiting impatiently for Michael's return as the afternoon wore on and turned into evening. Michael then called, I knew instantly he'd had a few too many beers, I could hear it in his voice, 'Hi babe, I'm with Annette and her dog.'

'Yes.' I replied, un-amused. *Was the dog driving them home?* I thought. Michaels 'get-me-out-of-jail' was: " I'm with Annette and her dog, don't worry luv". I wasn't one bit interested in what he had to say. 'When are you coming back?'

'Well, that's the problem; I left your car parked outside someone's garage.' Slight pause. 'The bad news is, it's been towed, but don't worry, because there's good news.'

'What do you mean, my Beetle convertible has been towed? Towed where?' I asked now fully paying attention to what the good news could possibly be.

'Don't panic, the good news is I'm with Annette.'

'Yes, I know that.' Now my patience was running out.

'She knows where the car's been towed to.' *Great* I thought, *my car has been towed and two piss heads and a dog are about to pick it up.*

'Michael, leave it, you and Annette can get it tomorrow, just come back to the bar.' I insisted. He returned back to the bar, later that day, pissed and unable to work. Both Annette and Michael picked the car up the very next day, and paid the 80 euro fine. Annette was full of apologies, so was Michael; they each blamed each other. But as far as Michael was concerned, he had gained himself three new friends, Dinie being his favourite. She now visited our bar and joined Michael for a drink after he finished work. Later, I also became good friends with her and looked forward to her return each summer, especially for San Juan.

'What time are we meeting tonight, for San Juan?' Dinie asked on the telephone.

'8 o'clock, at the bar, bring a chair; I have some snack food and we're taking the tables from the bar. Oh, and some wine, I have a cooler box.'

'Of course, I'll bring some bubbly.' She said.

'Pat's bringing his *Jackybiatty*.' I informed. This was a hot spicy meat dish, which he makes different each time he cooks it, depending on the left-over herbs and spices stored away in his kitchen cupboard.

'I look forward to it.' Dinie then hung up. Michael arrived with the wood and plonked it down on our terrace.

'We're not doing a BBQ this year, last year it was so dark I couldn't see to cook the food and then half of it fell on the sand. I think the only one who ate it was Barry.' Michael stressed on.

'That's only because Barry was pissed.' Barry was another regular at the bar. He was like *Mr Ben,* he took his hat off to most jobs: one day he was a taxi driver, another day a painter, another day a satellite engineer and in his spare time, he liked a beer and a football match supporting Tottenham but were forgive him for that. 'Is Barry coming tonight?' I asked.

'Yeah, his mates are over from England, the golfers.'

'Ah, that's good; there should be a crowd of us, then. I best leave and get Sarina from school; I'll be back just before 8 o'clock.'

'Don't be late Jo. Oh and bring some coats for when it's cold later.'

I got to the school just in time before Sarina came out. Sarina had settled in to Spanish life and school quite comfortably. She had grown up and out this past year, looking a little tubby. I had put this down to *Comedor* (school dinners); the dinner ladies insist that the children should eat all their food. Sarina loves the Spanish food, so there was never a problem about her wasting any.

During the day she lives her life as a Spanish child,

and of an evening she is my little Essex girl. A lot of the English children had left the school because of the crisis, returning back to England with their families. Sarina didn't rely on the English children for friends; she mixed mainly with the Spanish children in her class. 'When are we going to the beach, Mummy? Is it San Juan now?'

'Later darling. Not until 8 o'clock tonight.' I answered, dragging her along by the hand, I was in a rush.

'Is that when we go in the sea and jump over the fire?'

'No, that's at 12 o'clock.'

'Are other children going?'

'Maybe.' I answered unsure of the answer. As Sarina was growing up, I noticed she was spending more of her time in adult company. It was difficult to find friends in my own age bracket because many of the English who lived here were of retirement age. Young British expats could never find work, so they didn't stay long. One had to be hard-working, with a strong stamina, to survive living and working in Spain. I believe if you can own and run your own business here successfully, you can survive anywhere in the world. 'Vincente and Lynda are going.' I knew Sarina loved their company, especially when Vincente screamed his MEOW. Strangely, Sarina always spoke English with Lynda and within an instant would switch to Valenciano Spanish with Vincente. His local village dialect was obviously easier for her to understand as his English was far too fast for her to follow.

San Juan, the fiesta on the beach; this is the one time in the year bon fires on the beach are permitted. People gather fire wood during the day in preparation for San Juan when hundreds of fires are lit from Denia to Valencia. This particular fiesta evening of the year is my favourite, celebrating midsummer night; it's the shortest night of the year and welcomes the summer. According to tradition, one is to jump over the fire three times at midnight or for the not so brave, to jump over three waves of the sea; as a result one will be cleansed and purified, problems will burn away. In addition, wishes can be written on to a piece of paper and casted into the fire for them to come true.

The beach opposite our bar was packed. We timed it just right to get a place and light our fire. Sarina was already in the sea. It was a warm evening to start, but as darkness drew in it became chilly. I noticed a lot of people dressed in white. *Were we meant to do this?* I asked myself. *Next year!*

'Sarina, come and get dry.' I called, 'Come and write your wishes.' Once she heard 'wishes' she came running, telling me she wanted a shop full of lipsticks. Her second and third wishes were for a chocolate shop and to appear on the program The Apprentice. It was now pitch dark; luckily I had brought some oil-filled candles and a battery-operated CD player for music. We were all tucking into Pat's Jackybiatty; it was perfect for the occasion, hot and spicy. Michael had already drunk far too much and needed the toilet, so Sarina took him to a bar on the beach; she led the way into the darkness with a torch. It was quite funny to watch a five-year old, holding her daddy's hand, leading him to the toilet, wobbling as he walked along the sand. I kept an eye out for the pair of them, and waited upon their return that took a while, but they were both back in time.

12 o'clock midnight had arrived, fleets of people made their way to the sea, holding hands as they jumped the waves. 'Mummy, Pat's still got his shoes on.' I looked across towards Pat who could barely stand, let alone jump a wave. But he managed it until his knee gave way and half his body fell into the ocean. Sarina nearly fell over herself with laughter. 'Mummy, I think Pat's drunk.' Sarina strolled over to help Pat gain his balance. She led him back to our table of food and drink. His trainers were now covered in wet sand and looked a sight. He slumped into a plastic chair that then gave way and the chair leg snapped. Now Pat was in a mess, covered in sand and barely recognising Michael, who now joined him in laughter, holding out his hand to help him up. The scene got worse: Pat had now pulled Michael over into the sand, what a sight. Vincente screamed out with excitement, 'Meow.' attracting nearly half the beach. Lynda nearly fell off her chair in uncontrollable laughter. The scene was like something out of a Laurel and Hardy

film. I was not amused especially as I was the one responsible for taking these drunkards home.

'No, Sarina, leave them there.' Sarina had gone to their rescue, but soon returned upon my instruction. 'Michael, I think it's time to leave.' I strongly suggested.

'Ok, luv whatever you say.' Pat replied, before Michael could and then joined in.

'Yes luv, I'm coming, its Pat, he's anchored me down.' Both men stumbled to stand, I looked at Sarina and said 'Shall we take these two home or leave them here?'

'Mummy, let's leave them,' a slight pause. 'Joking, joking.' With that we all left, Dinie helped and took Michael's hand and I guided Pat and Sarina.

This is what I call a beach party: people staying out all night, partying. The previous year we had been out till five in the morning, the passing of time is easily forgotten on San Juan's special fiesta day. While we were leaving, fireworks lit up the sky, the beaches were full of fire and fun.

The next day we all woke up, still covered in sand from the night before. 'Are you opening the bar?' I asked Michael.

'No, you are, I'm working late tonight.' he replied, turning over in bed, and placing the pillow over his head. *Shit I'd forgot, live music tonight. Damn it* I thought, *I've got to open up and return later tonight and work*. It was always a long shift when we had live music. I dragged myself out of bed, showered to wake myself and then left Sarina and Michael both in bed.

I arrived at the bar the same time as Jenny. 'Jenny, do you want to work tonight?'

'No Jo, I'm out with my mates.' *Damn it,* I thought again. *Who else could I ask? Lyn was away and only liked to work the odd shift that suited her, and Anne had left.* I felt shattered, I'd already worked a seven-day week as it was, and I needed a break.

Later, that morning Scarlett came in for her normal vodka and coke, no ice. 'Scarlett, do you know anyone who'd work for me tonight?'

'Oh, I don't know, let me think. Yes Pete's got himself a new boyfriend, Ryan. He's over here in Spain on a long term holiday, I'm sure he's looking for something to do.' Scarlett was an estate agent and knew everyone. She had lived in Spain for over twenty years, now retired and only working with rented properties, the intention being an easier life.

So a couple of hours later, Scarlet took me to meet Ryan. What a hunk, piercing blue eyes, fit with a 'six-pack' and a great personality to match it all. Sadly Gay! So it was all arranged and he started work that night.

'Michael, I'm taking the night off, I've got cover, Pete's new boyfriend is working, he's starting at seven, so be kind and welcome him. Oh, and tell Pat if he starts taking the piss, I'll be after him, that goes for all the guys.'

'Ok, Ok, he's whose boyfriend?' I then hung up the

phone with Michael shouting, 'He's gay. Jo wait.' Yes, we owned a bar that was now mainly male dominated during the day with football, playing on our large-screen television, we still offered breakfast, lunch, and music at the weekend and a bingo and quiz night.

The football lads welcomed our new bar man; he was assertive, clean, tidy and hardworking, and ignored any banter of the punters. In fact, they became quite protective towards him; no one could say a bad word against our Ryan.

Our live music was Chloe Elena, a black singer who begins her show impersonating Shirley Bassey whilst singing and walking around our bar to find an innocent man, then sits on his lap, stroke his head attentively, and still singing, she would neck his pint of beer in less than 5 seconds. During her act she would sit down, change her make-up, pull off her wig to expose a spikey mop, unzip her dress to then mutate into Tina Turner. No time was spared; this girl could sing, dance and finish her show on a cartwheel performing the splits, all in a small area that was our bar. Wow, what a show girl she was!

I enjoyed the evening sitting and relaxing amongst my friends Vincente, Lynda and Dinie. Pat had left early that evening, probably to cut a crooked deal somewhere, which wasn't often. I never asked, because I didn't want to know; he knew I wouldn't like it. Ryan settled in straight away, as if he was meant to be there. Michael had to agree that at last we had found the perfect bar man.

I began my search for a buyer; several people were interested in the bar. Paul and Ally showed some interest, but nothing came of it. Pat went through some figures with us, but we convinced him it wasn't such a good idea for a man of his age to buy a bar. The summer was drawing towards an end and still we had found no one. Until, one day out of the blue, right under our noses; Ryan showed some interest; he had worked a summer for us and was aware of how busy the bar was and he wanted an investment for himself and Pete. So the bar was sold!

* * *Denia Hair Nails & Beauty* * *

The empire begins. In April 2006 I find the perfect shop, three doors down from the bar. I'd had my eye on it for a couple of years and watched tenants come and go. Now it was my turn. I felt a little apprehensive at first; mainly because I was going to be self-employed and legally a business was not cheap to set up. To start with, I needed a licence; this could cost anything between 850 to 2,000 euros, depending on the type of licence required and whether it is a straightforward name change or a complete change in the type of activity. Also there was the social security (national insurance) tax to consider, a monthly payment of 254.21 euros, in addition to which there is shop rent, utility bills and accountancy fees. So one could understand why people worked illegally. I was the first English hair and beauty salon to set up in Denia, now I understood why!

So I could start a new business without financial worry, Michael returned back to his old job in England selling tools to engineering companies. A few of our friends commuted back and forth to England so we thought we'd give this opportunity a go. But for us this was going to be difficult as Michael didn't do shift work; he couldn't work one month on and then one month off, like some of the commuters. His job was Monday to Friday, so he travelled back to Spain, late on a Friday night, and returned on the Sunday evening flight. This only gave us two days together, once a fortnight. At first he rented at a bed and breakfast, then progressed to renting a room at our friend's house. It wasn't an ideal situation but we had to give it ago.

Sadly Michael had to leave the same day that I got the keys to the salon; It was like being a single mother once again, having to start up a hairdressing salon as I did, when Louis was as young as Sarina was then. I felt alone but determined to succeed in this venture and make it a long-term business, unlike the bar. So, to begin with, I decorated the shop and organised the salon fitments. Red was the colour I chose for the salon. The furniture was much more expensive compared with English prices. Yet again we were taking yet another gamble. It was to be the last one, if this didn't work we would all need to return back to England.

Our next calamity was my much beloved VW Beetle car. We couldn't afford the repayments and the time had come to relinquish it; we had to accept the reality of our situation. So we re-placed it with a Ford Focus. During this time I felt my life was like a game of snakes and ladders. We were landing on snakes and couldn't reach the ladders.

Without even realising it, Pat was supportive. Responsibility was never his ambition.

'I've got you a fridge, like you wanted.' Pat struggled to get the words out, he was out of breath, holding a fridge in his bare arms, stumbling his way through the salon door. 'This will do won't it, twenty euros.' He bartered, looking as though he was about to keel over, sweat covering his chest and back.

'Sold, I'll have it. Nice one Pat, I knew you'd find us a fridge.' Even though it was old and rusty, it worked and did the job. I placed my paintbrush down to show Pat where I wanted the fridge to go. *Out of sight* was my first thought.

'How you getting on? Looks good, looks like you've nearly finished. Do you fancy a glass of wine?' This was like music to my ears.

'Yeah, why not, I only have that wall to finish. What do you think of the furniture?' I asked.

'Red suits your personality. Positively, come on, I'll buy you that wine. Have you heard from Micky?'

'Yes, yesterday. I wish he was here to see my opening day.' I muttered whilst in deep thought; we hadn't seen each other now for two weeks. Michael had lots to sort out in England, and he wanted to get settled before returning back for a weekend.

'Come on, I'm here.' Pat assured me and led the way to our old bar.

The boys had done it up nicely, they changed the bar to a restaurant, got rid of the football and quiz, to concentrate on their cooking and the bingo. 'Hello Jo, how are you?' asked Pete in his Scottish accent. He was as handsome as Ryan. The two guys made a handsome couple.

'I'm fine, missing Michael though.' Pete ran round the bar to serve us.

'I'm sure. How's the decorating coming along.' Pete was good at changing the subject to a more positive one.

'Fine, I'm nearly done now, and Pat got me a fridge, although he nearly gave himself a hernia delivering it.' I joked. 'But I got some where to put my milk now.' Colin then entered the bar and joined us.

'Alright Jo, can you book us for a haircut?' Colin asked.

'Sure, when?'

'Now? Well finish your wine, I'll have a beer please mate.' Pete went off to serve him.

'You'll be my first customer.'

'Great. How's Mike?' he asked.

'In England, working; he's back next weekend.'

'Have you split up?'

'No. Why?' *Why would he think that?*

'I was just asking, I don't know why I thought that.' He was stuttering over his words, very unlike Colin. Normally he was so sure of himself, *but why would he think Michael and I had split up? Was that the gossip?* I thought. Pat then changed the topic to football, before I could take the subject any further.

We finished our drinks and went to the salon leaving Pat behind.

'The salon looks good Jo.' Colin commented.

'Come on I'll show you around. This is the beauty room.' A room sealed off from the rest of the shop, with its own door.

'This is the nail bar.' The nail bar was by the window that advertised our nail treatments. The rest of the salon was equipped for hairdressing: four red hydraulic chairs with a silver finish, matching mirrors and workstations. The basins were in the far left of the salon and reception was by the shop door near the entry. I was now feeling quite excited about the shop and had forgotten the earlier conversation concerning Michael and me.

Price lists were printed and a six-month radio advert was on air four times a day plus a six-month advert went into Female Focus, the local expat magazine. Our savings didn't last long; it was now the 'make or break' chapter in our plan to live in Spain.

Thinking with my British mentality I began with three English girls renting space off me; : a nail technician, a beautician and a hairdresser. I made one mistake; I chose three strong personalities, who all wanted what I had. For me this soon became a disaster!

The salon took off really well that first summer with a mixture of clients, mainly English, Spanish, French and an assortment of other nationalities. I had to improve my Spanish speaking, so I took up lessons with a crazy Spanish woman, Isabel, large, bubbly, full of life and zest. She screamed with joy when I spoke correctly, but she also screamed at me when I got it wrong. All in all, she was a great teacher.

I was also working for Marcella doing the weddings; we needed to earn as much money as possible. Although I enjoyed the wedding work and it took me to some lovely classy hotels in Altea and Calpe, I wasn't so keen on driving to them. Most of the time I managed to share a lift with the make-up artist, Maria, an ex-Miss world model who was from Venezuela. Fabulous looking woman, all legs and walked as though she was still on the catwalk. We hit it off straight away; she was 'Mother Nature' who ate and lived healthfully, whilst I was an Essex girl who loved to drink chardonnay and party.

We often travelled on the N332 to the hotels, to avoid the expense of tolls making for a colourful and more interesting journey.

'I wouldn't fancy that job.' I remarked, one day, as we travelled along the N332. A young girl sat on a white plastic chair just alongside an orange grove. She was obviously prepared for the hot day ahead of her, as she had barely anything on.

'What job?' Maria answered. Not taking her eyes off the steep mountain road.

'Selling oranges, in this heat.'

'Jo, she's not selling oranges, she's selling her bodily wares.' As Maria finished her sentence, she fell into complete laughter leaving me stunned. *Oh my god,* I thought, *she's a prostitute.* As we passed her, I looked back over my shoulder, and acknowledged her, now standing next the white chair with bum cheeks hanging out of a skimpy pair of shorts, obviously to attract potential clientele. As far as I was concerned, she was still selling fruit, the fruits of her forest!

Before the AP7 motorway was built, everyone used the N332, so several whore houses took up business along this road, otherwise known as 'night clubs'. Then disaster struck, when the new motorway was built taking business away from the 'night clubs'. So the girls had to become mobile; now they sit and wait for their business, always on a white plastic chair, and often enough by an orange grove, as there are plenty of them along the N332.

Each wedding was different, some small, others were large and some were demanding, not many I have to say. If a bride arrived as "bridezilla", Maria and I would charm and change her into a "princess bride". Marcella, the wedding organiser, had a great team of people working for her, consequently her business grew and with it, we did as well.

Financially the money was coming in but it was also

going out just as quickly. Another issue soon presented itself to me: Michael. During his odd weekend visits, he considered himself to be on holiday, spending time watching football in a bar and getting drunk. He gave neither Sarina or me any time or consideration; with the little time we had together, all we did was argue. I noticed we were growing apart and I was becoming more independent and more familiar with the single life. No attention was spared my way. I often asked myself if there was another woman.

* * *An affair?* * *

The temptation to have an affair myself often presented itself. I had become quite good friends with one of the reps from Madrid; he sold me hair colours in bulk for a good price and often called in the salon once a week, whether or not I needed anything. He spoke perfect English and had a mass of tight, curly black hair. For the first six months, he visited the salon every week and always left without a sale, until one Monday evening he came into the salon after Michael and I had an argument the previous night.

We had realised there was no money in what Michael was doing; our money was being wasted on flights, room rent and his social life; when he spent his weekends in England, he was lonely and bored. So this exercise was costing us money, money that we didn't have. I suggested that he gave up his job and return to Spain to find work, he wasn't happy with my suggestion. He had started a new life in England and enjoyed what he had. For him it was the best of both worlds: every other weekend he was a single man going out without the stresses and responsibility of family life around him and the following weekend he had his family and his home comforts waiting for him, together with the sunshine and his social life.

On this particular Monday I was upset and alone in the salon when Juan entered the shop; he could see I had been crying.

'Hola, I thought you might have gone home by now. I saw your lights still on?.' Juan asked with a concerning look. It was six in the evening; the girls had already finished their work and had left. Sarina was staying the night at Jane and Cole's, as there being no school the following day.

'I was just finishing.' I wiped my face and looked away so he couldn't see the upset.

'Do you want to go for a drink?' he asked.

'No, I have to go.' I replied and began to switch everything off; then I had a change of mind, Why not? I thought.

'Is this your way of selling me colours, get me tipsy so I don't care what I buy?'

'No, of course not, but I can sell them to you if you want?' He replied, cheekily.

'No, I'll settle for that drink.' I followed him in my car to a Spanish bar along the Las Marinas road. It was a bar I often passed, but had never visited. It was small and very smoky as we entered; dark wood covered all the walls with wooden beams above us. They sold pizza like it was out of fashion; I noticed all the tables had plastic tablecloths, striped in blue and white. All the furniture was wooden, not a plastic chair to be seen. Pictures of horses covered the walls; it became obvious to me that the owner was mad on horses.

'Is this where you come to eat or drink?' I asked, still taking in the scene.

'Yes, my aunty owns it. She's mad on horses.' He noticed me take a closer look at her photos.

'What do you want?' he asked. 'Are you hungry?'

'No, I'm fine, just a wine, please.' I had no appetite. *What was I doing here?* I asked myself, *with a man I barely knew, while my husband was working away. Maybe he had found himself another woman, maybe that's why he didn't want to be with his family.* All these questions were popping up in my mind as they had done before. Michael had suggested during our argument that to save money he would to fly out less frequently; every three weeks opposed to two. That was nearing once a month, was it worth staying married, I had asked. Juan broke my thoughts with a glass of wine.

'So you like horses?' he asked.

'Yes ,I used to have horses; I bought my first horse myself, when I was fifteen years old. I was inspired by the film *'International Velvet.'* I had forgotten that I'd done that. We chatted for an hour or more. Juan had led a similar life to me, he too had a son, at the same age as I had, nineteen. So we had lots to chat about. He had been in several long relationships; I wasn't sure if he was in one at the time. I didn't like to ask in case he got the wrong idea. All the same, I was attracted to and charmed by this Spanish man.

'So Jo, you look happier now, would you like another drink?'

'No thanks, I really need to make a move, and I will be buying some colours off you.'

'A move where?'

'Sorry, that's just an English expression.' Although Juan's English was very good, he didn't quite understand the English humour. 'It means I have to go.'

'But, why? You said your daughter's at her friend's. Stay for another.' I dared not, I felt myself flirting and coming out of my comfort zone. *Another wine, I would then need a taxi, then would Juan want to join me?* No, I was in fear of treading on dangerous ground.

'Really I must go,' *Quickly, think of an excuse.* 'It's my cat; he's been shut in all day.' *Pathetic excuse Jo,* I thought, but it was too late. Already I was up, off the bar stool, putting my handbag over my shoulder.

'Ok, you want to do this another time?' *Do what I thought? He must have read my mind.* 'Have a drink or dinner?' *Of course,* that's what I thought, *what else was there to think?* Why was I feeling guilty? But now he was beginning to sound like he was asking me out on a date.

'Sure,' what else was there to say? He followed me out of the restaurant to my car. *Please god, don't let him kiss me.* My thoughts and emotions were all over the place. 'Thanks Juan, I needed that.' *Needed what?* Again I asked myself. *Attention, a shoulder to cry on or just male company?*

'No problem.' He leant forward and kissed each of my cheeks, squeezing my arm whilst doing so. It felt good; shit, in a way I wished he had kissed me.

'I'll come in next week with a good deal on colours.' he said, as he walked back to his car. Maybe he wasn't flirting with me; maybe he did only want to sell me hair colours.

The drive home seemed endless. *I'll call Michael when I get home,* I thought. *Hopefully he'll reassure my feelings.* But there was no answer, I called several times and then tried the house,he rented. No answer there either. *Shit, what a mess, where was he?* He always answered his mobile. I called all night, both numbers and then gave up by eleven. I assumed he [1] didn't want to talk to me or [2] he was with her.

That was it, I was now convinced there was another woman, I searched for the evidence: mobile phone bill first. After looking through several sheets of listed numbers, there it was, a late call on a Sunday night. *Who would call him at around eleven on such a night?* I asked myself. It was a night he would have been travelling home on, maybe just flying into Stansted Airport. Perhaps she was waiting for his return. Naturally I did what any Essex girl would do, I called the number the next day.

It was lunchtime when I decided to make the fatal call. I felt sick, my stomach was doing somersaults, I couldn't leave it any longer, I needed to know; would she even admit to any thing?

'Hello,' Silence, the phone switching to answer machine.

'Hello, this is Jessica Parker, sorry I am unable to answer your call, please feel free to leave a message and I shall return your call. Bleep, bleep, bleep.' Then I waited and waited, *Fuck it, I'd already judged and 'jewelled' her.*

'Hello, this is Michael Blackford's wife. Are you fucking around with my husband? If so, you can keep him, you wouldn't be the first nor the last.' I hung up and cried in the confines of my staff room. Luckily all the girls were out of the salon, having a coffee next door probably, checking each of their strategies on how to take Jo's business from her, given her marriage had already been wrecked.

I washed my face and reapplied my make-up so that no one noticed my tears. My phone rang several times and then the salon phone rang. 'If it's Michael, can you tell him to call back later?' He did, just as I was locking up the salon.

'Jo, what the hell are you doing calling up a colleague from work and accusing her?'

'Where were you last night?' I broke into his sentence. 'You didn't answer your phone and I know you weren't at home either.'

'Jo, calm down, I was down the pub, I'd had too much to drink and slept in my car.'

'Bullocks.' I hung up. I knew he was lying, it would have been far too cold for him to stay in his car, *Does he take me for some kind of fool?* The phone rang again and again.

'Jo, I swear I'm not lying. I can't believe you called Jessica up.'

'Michael, why would she call you at eleven o'clock at night, and on a Sunday?'

'What night? A Sunday, It was probably to do with work, she's a new rep, I'm helping her. You are so embarrassing. You never trust me.' I hung up the phone, I was hurting and I didn't want to listen to any more of his lies.

Once I'd calmed down I got onto the internet and booked a flight to England for myself and Sarina. I felt like a break and I needed to speak to Michael to clear this once and for all.

So two days later there we were in cold, wet weather, England. I surprised Michael with a call. 'Can you pick us up from the airport?'

'Airport, what airport?'

'Stansted, your daughter and I are here. That's if you remember us.' I said sarcastically.

'Jo, don't be like that, I'm leaving now.' An hour later, he was there waiting in arrivals. *He still looks good back in his suit,* I thought. Sarina ran over to him.

'Daddy, daddy. I love you daddy.' Couldn't beat a bit of daughterly love, hopefully that should remind him of what he was about to lose. He hugged me and kissed my cheek.

'I'm staying at my mother's,' before he asked.

'Ok, can I stop there too?' I could see he'd missed us both, maybe he was telling the truth, maybe I'd over reacted as I sometimes do. Also, from where he was staying was an hour's drive away from my mother's house.

'We'll see. We need to sort things out, we can't keep doing this, there's no money in it, you don't earn enough to commute. And you say there's not another woman but what do you expect me to think, when you want to stay here in England, working and spending our money on expensive flights and beer.' Well, that was how it felt.

'Jo, let's just see how it goes till after Christmas, I'll try and put some money away. It gives us another three months, and I promise not to go out, but it's lonely here at weekends, what do you expect me to do, sit in my room?' Maybe he had a point, I thought.

'I'm here for a couple of days; we need to sort something out.' I wasn't completely convinced and as for the Jessica tart, maybe she just was someone at work. I remember that Michael had mentioned a young girl starting at work and he had also mentioned she having a crush on him. Quite honest of him but what was I to believe? Only that I would be keeping a close eye on him.

The next couple of days too soon passed and Michael was already returning us back to the airport. He had convinced me that there wasn't another woman and that he wanted us to join him in England permanently. But I was still following 'the dream' and I was sure that the salon was our future, having only opened it 6 months ago it was already showing a promising income.

'Daddy, when are you coming home?'

'Next week, babe.' Sarina missed her father; they have a very close relationship and I could see the effect the current situation was having on her. We kissed goodbye at the gate before joining the incredibly long queue that lay ahead. The dread of flying then took hold of me again, despite not having noticed it on the flight out, blanketed by the built up anger inside of me. With Michael's reassurance, telling me how much he loved me and I was the only one for him, the situation was more or less resolving itself. This put a smile on my face, so just before boarding I decided to call him to tell him, that I loved him too. But when the time came the phone rang and rang without answer. I tried once more but his phone was now switched off. *Shit, he was with her.* This stabbed me in the heart, my chest tightened with panic. I hadn't even left the country and already he'd gone to her. I instinctively felt this.

The flight back was terrible, I felt sick with all my fears, so I ordered two large vodkas hoping they would help ease the hurt and fear I was feeling. Instead, it just made me feel emotional. Sarina had fallen asleep leaving me to chat to an old lady who sat next to me. She looked very old and had lots of wrinkles, too old to be travelling alone. She smelled of lavender, was immaculately dressed and spoke the Queen's English. I had the perfect candidate right beside me so I told her my whole life story. She was very sympathetic and listened to everything I had to say throughout the flight, agreeing to my every word. Although I must say, she did make an inelegantly fast exit off the plane, giving the excuse that her son was waiting for her and that she mustn't be late. By this point I was worn out lacking oxygen from too much talking and she must have had an earache. We flew through Arrivals and Customs; there was no hassle about being delayed. My face must have said it all: UPSET!

My friend Lydia was waiting for me, outside the airport, she noticed me straight away as I waved over to her. It was dark and there was a chill in the air. Lydia brought the car round. I loaded Sarina and our luggage into it; once we began the journey home, she fell back into a deep sleep. Sarina had been a dead weight during the whole journey and my back had ached from lifting her. I told Lydia all that had happened transpired.

'Bastard.' was her only reply. I tried calling Michael's phone again, it was late at night and his phone was still switched off. I then called the house from which he was renting a room. My friend answered and said he wasn't home. It had been five hours ago since he'd dropped me off at Stansted airport. *Where the hell was he and was he with her?* Of course he was. Lydia had also said so; but she didn't like most men and she was always negative. Nothing was ever half full in her glass, physically or mentally, she always jested it was 'fucking half empty.' That was only because she never left a drink long enough in it to be anything else. But she was a good friend who I felt needed someone like me around her to give her positive energy, although at the time I was out of it myself.

A week passed; my phone held a list of unanswered calls and text messages. I had been betrayed yet again. I couldn't speak to him. I was losing weight, unable to eat, and I avoided the wine as I needed to keep my head on my shoulders. Turning to the bottle would only have weakened me, I had to stay strong and deal with my situation, as well as having to deal with 'the three witches of Eastwick' at work.

I had decided to take them out one at a time, without them even realising. I would let them believe they were leaving on their terms, when secretly I was already one step ahead of each of them. I was diplomatic all the way.

Eventually, I let Sarina answer the phone to her Daddy; it wasn't her fault that this situation had happened. Michael spoke to her for an hour; I could tell he was upset on the phone listening to the way Sarina spoke to him. She assured him that I wasn't ready to speak to him and that when I was, I'd call him. She was so grown-up for six, she took each day as it came, nothing ever fazed her. All was fine as long as she was able to do what she wanted.

Juan had popped in several times; I bought a batch of colours of him for a good price. He asked me out for coffee on each visit but I was busy with clients, which in a way suited me at the time. I couldn't handle any more stressful situations, even though he did put a smile on my face and I was quite flattered.

One morning as I drove to work after dropping Sarina off, my phone rang. It was Michael. I'd put him off long enough, so I pulled the car over to answer knowing it was now time for me to speak with him and knowing exactly what I was going to say.

'Jo, hello, hello.'

'Yes Michael.' I answered in a cool manner.

'At last, you're speaking to me. Please let me explain. Before you hang up, Jo, I was on the motorway when you called, I couldn't answer the phone, there was thick fog when I was driving home and weather warnings, and so I drove back and stayed with my brother. You can ask him.' I thought back to that heart-wrenching night; it's true that time is a healer; my heart had since reasoned with the event of that flight, until now.

'Then why didn't you call me, why did you turn your

phone off?' I asked, now with tears in my eyes and an aching in my stomach.

'My battery ran out and I didn't have my charger. Jo I love you, I haven't eaten all week, you won't answer my calls, and if you want me to come back I'll come back tomorrow.'

'Ok, then do that.' I called his bluff, this wasn't what I was going to say. After listening to his story I didn't know what to believe, only that I still loved him and if he meant what he just said, I would hold him to it.

'Jo, if I do that then I won't be paid, I have to give notice, you know that and if I leave without notice, then they'll never take me back in the future.' But there was no future for us if he stayed there. We couldn't carry on living apart, it wasn't even cost affective. What was he holding onto?

'Michael, come back or stay there, you have till this weekend to decide. If you don't then we need to split up. If you decide to stay in England, then I would have to deal with it. Financially, we are not benefitting and our marriage is falling apart. As for Sarina, we would need to make sure that it didn't affect her. I'm sorry, but I can't carry on like this. It's not fair on either of us, I'm sure you can find some work here.' There was silence, 'Michael, I have to go, I'll be late for work.'

'Ok, if that's what you want. I love you and I always will.' He then hung up. I burst into tears, *What had I done?* I was late to work that morning!

The salon was busy, everyone chatting. I was quiet; I think the girls knew something was wrong but I wasn't about to share my private life with them. I just listened to them asking clients for their contact details to keep them on record for the salon's benefit if there was a change of appointment or if there was a promotion, then clients could be easily contacted. I knew better. I had been a salon owner before, and I wasn't stupid. On this particular day I couldn't be bothered, *They could take the whole business and my money as well.*

Colin came in for his usual hair cut, he was always the last client. The girls had already packed away and left.

'Alright, Jo?' He asked, as he sat himself down into my cutting chair.

'I'm fine, well I will be if Michael comes home this weekend.' I then told Colin the complete story whether he wanted to hear it or not, he got it. He had always been close with Michael, often keeping him out till early hours of the morning, after a night shift in our bar with Dinie.

'Jo, he'll be back. He'd be a fool not to.' That was all the advice Colin could muster which didn't make me feel any the better; he paid and then left.

'Is daddy home tomorrow, Mummy?' The weekend soon came round; I'd not heard anything from Michael and I couldn't bring myself to calling him, let alone chase after him. I had offered him his freedom, an ultimatum, now it was his decision to stay in England or to return home to his family.

'I don't know babes, let's wait and see.' I turned the key to unlock all of the four locks to our front door. I felt tired and my heart ached; it had been a long day and a busy one, it was Friday. I started the log fire; Lyn had shown me how to light a fire before she left to return to England She suggested the northern style, wrapping a firelighter in newspaper, twisting it in and out of the wood. Her husband had received a great job offer in Saudi Arabia on the rigs and this meant joining him there on a permanent basis. He wouldn't have had the lengthy time off that he was used to, so naturally he wanted his wife nearby. This saddened me, another friend lost. But not forever!

'Mummy, Mummy, Daddy's outside.' Sarina screamed with excitement. *Oh my god, he's come home.* I instantly thought as I opened the door, my stomach doing a somersault. There he was, still in his suit from work, holding his cases. It was dark outside and late. The fire was now on its cinders with the telly blaring music to the credits of an old movie that Sarina and I had been watching.

'You know we've got no money now, I'm not going to get paid this month, I hope you've got some.' He hugged me tightly and told me he loved me. Part of me was relieved, but a part was concerned and that part had nothing to do with the money.

* * *The QROPS man* * *

Winter 2009 was upon us; business wise I'd had a great summer in the salon. Now the tourists had gone leaving only the locals that who lived here and who were becoming fewer and fewer each year. There were fewer middle-aged people around and work was becoming scarce. Even the car salesman had to leave for England with his family because of lack of work. A small percentage of pensioners were now picking up the cream by cleaning swimming pools, property maintenance and gardening, mainly. The credit crisis had taken away a lot of the un-desirables that wasn't a bad thing. There is no financial aid for the unemployed here in Spain; unless one has worked legally. As for the self-employed people, they were treated the same as in the UK.

Michael and I had begun to deal with our relationship. We loved each other equally but like most couples, we had taken each other for granted. As for Jessica, I had left her a voice message with strong advice using my Essex tongue. A message she won't ever forget.

Michael had decided to take a career in DJ'ing, but it was only part-time and didn't pay too well, especially as the bar owners like everyone else, was feeling the pinch. To earn some extra money we decided to go to the Rastro, (boot fair) and sell some of our unwanted items. We needed to do some thing now two months behind on our mortgage repayment. To add to this unpleasantness, the nearby building site was burning pallets of wood to save money. Our situation had become desperate.

It was a six o'clock start, 'Sarina, come on, get up, and you Michael.' I shouted, ordering the family into position for our first day of market trading.

The shouting and screaming began, 'Have you got loose change?' I asked.

'Yes, of course, do you want tea or coffee in the flask?' Michael asked as the kettle boiled.

'Coffee with sugar please.' I felt a little apprehensive, not knowing the *Rastro* procedure, i.e. where to go, what time was best to arrive and to whom did we pay the entry fee? But we were soon to find out. We were equally excited about selling our wares and making some money, especially Sarina. 'Sarina, go to the toilet before we leave.'

'I have.' She answered. Michael was now loading our last items. It was still dark outside; by the time we were ready to leave, the sun was rising. It was the middle of March so the weather could be a little unpredictable.

'Ok, all in?' Michael asked as were all now sitting in a car loaded inside to the roof, full of junk. He leaned over his shoulder to check on Sarina, all we could see was her face, everything was piled on top of her. Then he looked at me and laughed. 'Jo, look, we've even packed the cat.' I looked over my shoulder; Sarina began to join Michael in laughter. There was our cat crunched down, packed in the car. How ridiculous this all looked. I thought *Oh my god, we must be mad,* I laughed and I got out the car to let the cat out.

'Luckily you noticed him. I'd have died if he'd come to the market with us.'

As we nearly reached the entrance of the Rastro, we were suddenly facing a rather large queue, so we joined it. My first thought was that we were too late, but half an hour later we were paying the Spanish market attendant.

I hoped we had a good position; the market was set in a rather large carpark belonging to the El Vergel safari park. The *Rastro* was on every Saturday and Sunday. This particular day was a Sunday, not that either day mattered, as it was busy both days. The market stalls were set amongst willow trees over hanging the car park, which conveniently protected the stall holders from the sun's strong rays. There were a couple of cafeterias, a playground and a picnic area which helped make a day out for everyone.

We found our spot, squeezed our car between two other cars and began to set up. Within seconds, the Moroccans were upon us, '*Cuantes?*' (How much?) They were lifting items out of our car faster than us getting out of the car, we were surrounded, prices were coming out of my mouth left, right and centre, and I hadn't a chance to think.

'Sarina, hold onto my phone.' I took no chances, more Moroccans came and joined the fugue, harassing us to reduce the prices of our goods. Suddenly Michael took a stand; he grabbed everything out of their hands and pointed for them to stand back and wait. I grabbed what I could to put on our tables before another Moroccan arrived. We seemed to have taken control of our situation but not for long. We got quicker and stricter with our pricing, snatching items out of their hands if they didn't want to pay what we wanted. We were arguing over pennies, but like Vincente always says, 'a penny is a penny.'

It was 12 o'clock, we had nearly sold everything and we'd tamed the Moroccans. They grasped our sense of humour, especially when we told them they were 'bandidos.' (bandits). They liked this and laughed. After 4 hours bartering and selling half our junk, we sat and relaxed. 'Do you want a coffee now?' Michael asked as he went to the car,

'Are you sure you didn't sell the flask.' I answered jokingly.

'You say that, they even had my tool box and the jack to the car.' We both laughed about the morning's events. 'I can't believe you sold all those odd kitchen utensils,' Michael went on in palpable disbelief.

'I know, I just stuck them all together, 3 euros for

the lot. Mind you, by then I think the Moroccans were more scared of me' I joked. Even Sarina was taking money, god help us whether she had given out the correct change. We'd had a lucrative morning, and earned some money but sadly not enough to pay our mortgage.

We took it in turns to venture round the market on our own. I'd found myself chatting to a young girl on a stall opposite, an attractive girl, she had two young children with her; unfortunately, her husband had returned back to England leaving her as a single mother. She hadn't wanted to go back so for income she sold cheap knocked-off goods and jewellery to survive. I felt sorry for her as I knew that there would come a time when she too would have to return to England and in my thoughts, I was hoping that she didn't leave it too late. It's an unbearable situation when you can no longer feed your own children. Recently, I'd had sleepless nights worrying about money and our current situation. I'd wake in a panic, covered in sweat, experiencing yet another nightmare of living on the street with no money. In my mind I was not about to let this happen and I didn't care what it took to survive. My dream of living here in Spain was now like a nightmare.

We did the *Rastro* markets every Sunday. I also used this time as an advertising tool, having Sarina hand out the salon leaflets whilst we were there. I had successfully got rid of the 'three witches of Eastwick'. A new beautician had come on board, Lorraine, a quiet young woman with little ambition, until I had got hold of her giving her the drive that she needed. We worked well together and formed a nice friendship. Michael and I still hadn't caught up with our mortgage repayments. *Once we were back into the summer season, everything will be ok.* I kept telling myself.

One morning I received a call from an elderly gentleman asking me if I had a private pension. At the time I thought it was a hoax, but what did I have to lose, especially as he was sending me a guy with the same surname as my maiden name, so I kind of saw it as an omen. Gary Downs had himself an appointment.

Gary came to the salon late one evening, a smart man in a suit, similar age to me and with a good head of hair. Michael joined us towards the end of our meeting, just to check and see what it was all about. Naturally I was suspicious but Michael took it one step further and looked in to what this guy had to offer.

The QROPS (Qualifying Recognised Overseas Pension Scheme) is a way of moving private pensions overseas to New Zealand,with the facility to cashing it in tax-free or re-investing it. This package was only available to ex-pats who had lived overseas for more than 5 years and by this time, we had. We spoke with several people and as yet no one had taken the offer. Until Michael did; he saw it through to the end, and cashed in his private pension, into which he had paid for many years. It had been frozen up until this opportunity had presented itself. Michael received a large sum of money, completely tax-free. His pension had matured sooner than later. I then took up the package, as did several of our friends; the ball began to roll for the QROPS with many ex-pats taking advantage to release their pensions early. Now was a good time to reinvest the money for our futures. So Michael paid a lump sum off our mortgage and then set himself up as 'Denia All Services' offering property, gardening and swimming pool maintenance. He did a course in cleaning swimming pools and had gardening experience from working for my father, years ago, to buy my engagement ring. As for me, I reinvested my money back into the salon with the little left over to buy myself something I knew I wasn't allowed to have.

* * *Barclay! Saved from financial loss* * *

'I hope you haven't got what I think you have in that basket, Jo. I'll leave if you have.'

'Michael, leave your front door key on this table. I'm going to get myself a glass of wine and show my girlfriends my new puppy.' With that, I strolled past Michael and his beer buddies, who were sitting outside the local English bar, Café Hola, enjoying their pint of beer. Sarina passed them, shrugging her shoulders and with a grin that reached one side of her face to the other dismissing her father. As far as she was concerned, she was on my side that day. The girls were all seated on the opposite table, they screamed with joy when the puppy appeared.

That very day I had every intention of treating myself to a little male Yorkshire terrier whom I would call Barclay. It wasn't my fault Michael, as a child, had been bitten by a chihuaha and disliked dogs.

'So, mum, where did you say we were going?' Sarina, nagged; she hated the not knowing.

'Sarina, it's a surprise, wait and see, we're nearly there. Come on, one more road to cross.' I explained as

I grabbed her hand and led her on to the zebra crossing. Then we entered the pet shop. Her face lit up.

'Are we buying another gold fish?' she asked with excitement.

'No, we're buying a puppy.' My god, she nearly peed her pants.

'Really, mummy, really?'

'Yes, Sarina, I want a male Yorkshire terrier.' I explained as I guided her through the noise of a cockatiel, passing several reptile tanks, fish and then reached what I had come for, the puppy section. This was a dog I had always wanted, small enough to take to work and wear as a handbag, a typical Essex-girl accessory. I wanted all the glitz that went with him; I already had a name for him, Barclay, after the bank. I thought the name appropriate at the time, especially as I was using my Barclays pension fund to buy him; this would then be a constant reminder of where he'd come from.

There were two male puppies in a glass cage; they both looked very similar, little balls of fluff. Sarina held one, while I held the other. 'Mummy, they're both so cute, I'm so happy, I'm going to cry.' With that she did, tears rolled down her chubby cheeks. 'What about daddy?' She remembered; her face went into shock; her daddy had always said 'No dogs.'

'Oh, never mind daddy.' She then said with a cheeky smile. Squeezing the puppy to her face he licked her twenty to the dozen.

'Who cares about daddy, he'll just have to leave.' I said, knowing deep down he wouldn't. He just didn't like pets because they cost a lot and he hates to see his wife and daughter cry when they die. 'I think this is the one, he loves you already.' This dear little puppy lapped Sarina up. He was just as excited to be in her arms as she was to hold him. Barclay!

* * Moving to La Xara * *

After all the excitement of receiving our tax-free pensions, Michael decided it was time to move.

As for accepting Barclay, he just chose to ignore this little ball of fluff but to whom everyone gave too much attention. We had decided to rent our house out as a holiday home; it was more suitable for this and enabled us to move on and into a larger home. There were plenty advertised on the internet but none that suited our requirements. Until one day, Michael printed off the advertisement of a property to show me.

'It's in La Xara, what do you think? It's been renovated into an English style country cottage. I think I know where it is. Do you want to take a drive out?'

'Yeah, why not, it's Sunday.' In the meantime Michael had emailed the owners for a proper viewing inside. We drove into La Xara and found the property straight away.

'This is it; shall we have a look through the window?'

'Yeah, come on Mummy.' With that all three of us jumped out of the car and looked around as we approached the property. The curtains were drawn in the dining room, we could just about peep a look through.

'Looks old inside, do you think someone's died and left it empty?' I remarked,

'Mummy, look over here.' Sarina was at the garden gate, 'It's got a swimming pool.' The garden looked like someone's secret garden; it was a typical English garden from what we could see.

'Michael, when can we view it properly?' I asked, excitedly.

'Tomorrow, I sent an e-mail just as we left, to view it tomorrow.'

'Great, come on we'll come back tomorrow.' I was excited to view the whole property; something there intrigued me, I didn't know what exactly but I had a good feeling.

We returned the following evening. An agent met us at the property; she was a small woman, English. She had known the previous owner who sadly had died rather suddenly. The house was full of antiques, old furniture, and portraits. I loved it all, even the antiques, which surprised me as I had always chosen modern furnishings for my properties; maybe it was time for a change. 'When did the lady die?' I asked, thinking at the time it had been recent, as a lot of her stuff was still around in cabinets and old books were still in there.

'A couple of years ago, she left the house to her two daughters.' The property was like a shrine, I thought at the time. We were led through a country-style kitchen to the garden; instantly we could hear the cockerels next door, cockadoodledooing, one after the other, as if in tune. Then a neighbouring cockerel joined in. Sarina and I were in the Garden of Eden. English grass and shrubs as well as herb trees grew abundantly around a rather large swimming pool. Next to this was a wooden naya, filled with cane garden furniture stacked on top of each other for winter storage.

'Mum, luv it, luv it.' Sarina repeated with her Essex tongue. I had to agree, I had found "home".

We re-entered the house to view the upstairs, everyone leading the way while I was last still taking in my surroundings. Just as I took a couple of steps, I tripped up on the stone stairs,

'All right luv?' Michael called down.

'I'm fine; the steps are higher than normal.' I remarked and took more care. There were three rooms and two bathrooms; we entered the master room that had an en-suite resembling a small cave with a large walk in shower. It had been tastefully decorated and took Michael's attention. Sarina noticed a small curtain in the adjoining bedroom, she pulled it across to discover another set of stairs.

'Mummy, can I go up?'

'No, the agent snapped, there's nothing up there, only private stuff that belonged to the late owner.' Michael and I looked at each other, alarmingly. I took

Sarina's hand and led her away from the curtained-off area.

We had seen all we were able to see. 'Michael, I luv it, what do you think?' I asked as we got into our car and waved a goodbye to the agent.

It's old, too old; there was a rat in the garden. All those portraits, the furniture is not us, we like modern stuff, oh and it's haunted. What was that all about, when Sarina pulled that curtain open to another staircase? There's probably a body up there, or a ghost!'

'I can't believe you've said that. Yes you have a point about the curtained staircase. We can ask the daughters about that. Michael, I love it and so does Sarina.' I begged all afternoon and the next day, and the next week until I gave up. Michael didn't like it, 'Too old.' he kept saying. So he arranged for us to view other properties, modern ones.

'Jo, come on, please they're waiting to show us around.' Michael begged. He took me to view two or three other houses. I didn't like any of them and now it was time for me to make a stand.

'No, I'm not getting out; I have found the house we like.' I said sitting in the passenger side of our Ford Focus which was parked outside another modern property, near a couple patiently waiting at their front door, looking confused by my behaviour. Sarina had given up and decided to show herself around.

'Come on mum, you won't like it, just keep daddy

happy.' Both Michael and I looked at each other in disbelief as Sarina made her statement standing next to the in-patient couple.

'Ok, you can have the house under one condition; they take all that old furniture away; I want it empty. And you view this house right now.' Michael was desperate.

'I was going to anyway.' That I did in 10 seconds flat. Michael knew what he was up against and hoped the deceased's daughters wouldn't agree to remove all the furniture.

* * *Our new home* * *

On 1st December 2011 we had moved in. I arranged everything and refurnished our new home, alone. Michael wanted nothing to do with it until he decorated, my god he moaned but it was worth it. Even Michael had a sense of achievement now that he had put his "paw print" on the property.

The house had come alive again, it had seemed so sad the day we first viewed it. Now if was full of noise and laughter.

Our neighbours on both sides were Spanish. One had chickens which we eventually became used to hearing them, especially at 5 o'clock in the morning, the neighbour on the other side was the local village policeman and his family. Sarina was often invited by the policeman for Paella on Sundays; she preferred this to our Sunday roast. I sometimes wondered if he was the policeman in Derek Lamberts book; *Spanish Lessons.* I found out that indeed he was who portrayed himself as the *Pistolero*, (the gun man) who let his gun fire off in pursuit of a bank robber. Now, nearing retirement, he manages the school crossing, still armed, I hasten to say.

My daughter Sarina has often shared a wheelbarrow of oranges with him. Were they scrumping? I believe they were picked from the ground, and I wouldn't suspect anything else from a nearly-retired Spanish policeman and a nine year-old Essex girl.

As for the four legged neighbours, we decided to fence them off, for safety reasons.

* * Two dogs and a cat * *

We loved our new house and for the first time since living in Spain, I felt at home, like it was meant to be. Early one morning Sarina had gone out into the garden to fetch her flip flops for school which she had left by the swimming pool the previous night. She wasn't gone long as I could hear her steps race back from the garden. I put my head out the door as soon as I heard, 'Mum, quick, there's dog's in the garden.' Sarina rushed passed me and flew into the kitchen panting out of breath. I stepped out to take a look, all I could hear was dogs fighting, barking and yelping through the bushes of our garden. I instantly joined Sarina in the kitchen and shut the door. 'Mum, you've got to do something.' she cried in panic.

'Michael, Michael, quick there are dogs fighting in the garden.' Both Sarina and I looked out of the window and there we saw two German Shepherds attacking what we thought was a small dog, until we both looked again; the victim was a large ginger tom cat standing on its hind legs fighting for its life with claws lashing out at either side of each dog. 'Michael, quick, these dogs are going to rip this cat apart.' An instant vision came to mind: me clearing up the remains of a dead cat. The dogs yelped, I returned back to the kitchen door where Michael had now joined me.'Is it our cat?' he asked going outside picking up some large pebbles.

'I don't know.' I was too scared to look; everything was happening so fast. What if the dogs turned on us? Then the cat suddenly lost its balance and fell into our swimming pool. Now my vision was that of scooping out a dead, drowned cat. By now Michael was throwing rocks at the dogs who circled the swimming pool. I couldn't believe what I was seeing: a cat swimming the whole length of the pool. It dragged its self over to the sunbeds and laid itself down; as for the dogs, they'd left. I think Michael had frightened them off with the rocks, or maybe their owner had called them back from the campo that joined the bottom of our garden.

It wasn't our cat but it was the cat that had been living in the garden prior to our moving in. An ugly looking cat, with a scar across its face and owner of the largest set of balls I had ever seen (my god he'd used them that day). The cat survived and we felt it had earned its place in the garden as our guard cat. All the same, this episode didn't put us off living in this peaceful haven; Michael's unfunny remarks were ignored.

Michael's business grew month by month, the customers liked the way he conducted his business. He photographed every bit of evidence of work he did. Unlike a lot of ex-expats that had done property maintenance, a lot of them took money up front and then fled the country without carrying out any of the work.

Our relationship slowly repaired itself for the time being and living in the house in La Xara helped. Strangely, the property inspired me to pick up my writing of memoirs. After 8 months of writing, it was suggested I join a writing group.

So, like most of my contacts, I happened to cut Margaret's hair, who belonged to a writing group. Margaret encouraged the idea of my writing and as bad as my writing was to begin with, she never discouraged me. She is an older woman, who speaks the Queen's English. What I admire about her is that she never judges anyone and she has a large outlook on life because I think she's travelled a lot and lived in African countries, due to her late husband's job. She's an educated "lady" who taught English.

I attended the first meeting as a nervous visitor with 500 words of my book. The meetings took place at Sue's house in Denia; she was a retired schoolteacher, who writes quite passionately. Jean, who took the meeting, is an American woman who recently had her book published; she is a very inspirational lady, especially when it comes to writing. There were 9 to 10 members in the group; each member read out their 500 words that I found fascinating. Most of the members concentrated on short stories and enjoyed literacy books. David read his work out first; he had been a language teacher, now retired, but what a great writer and critic; he had written a humorous descriptive piece about a man and his shed. Then Irene's husband, Gordon, read her piece, I wondered at first why Gordon read her work, but it soon came clear: he reads very dramatically and clearly speaking the words precisely as they should sound, raising and lowering his voice to Irene's attentive writing. Gordon then read for Lorraine, as her eyesight isn't so good; he read her work with passion using his Sean Connery voice, one could easily imagine the story he read. I was next; too nervous to read, I passed my work over to David. I had chosen the first 500 words of my book and it sounded more like a synopsis with too much information in too few words, 'telling' and not 'showing' the story set out. The group critiqued my work with kindness.

I had joined the group as an Essex blonde, hairdresser, whereas each other member of the group, most were retired school teachers who held a degree in English literature. Had I gone in at the deep end?

Yes, of course I had, and nothing was going to stop me, even when the meetings were changed to a hotel for a short while, I turned up like a bad penny. I was not going to give up because of my lack of tertiary education, I was there to learn. At the time, I hazarded to guess their thoughts, 'what makes her think she's a writer?', 'does she have the stamina to write a book?', 'I give her a couple of months', 'what dream cloud is she on?'

Maybe the living in Spain is one!

* * *Where are they now?* * *

Conner and Patsy: They disappeared as they appeared, on the run!

Paul, Ally, Alex and Shelley: Returned to England for financial reasons.

Jenny: Returned to England to find a man.

Anne and Don: Returned to England, they missed their family.

Denzal: Sadly died. Zeta is living her life between England and Spain.

Lyn: Moved to Saudi Arabia due to her husband's job.

Barry: Still lives in Spain, changing hats.

Sharon: The maneater sadly died due to her recreational life style. A friendship missed.

Annette and Gomish: Still live in Spain. Sadly Gomish died, but she now has another dog.

Pete and Ryan: Returned to England. The bar is sadly closed.

Party-time Pat: Still parties in another country, only at weekends.

Glasgow Gary: Whereabouts unknown.

Lydia: Returned to England.

John the gardener: Still keeps his regular routine, living in Spain.

Colin: Returned to England.

Jane and Cole: Still surviving in Spain.

Madge and Sid: Madge returned to England and to her ex-husband. Sid lives somewhere in Spain.

Marcella: Lives in Spain, still successfully organises weddings and Blessings.

Maria: Her dream came true, she had a baby. Still offers make-up to Marcella's weddings.

Pat: Returned to England for his own benefit.

Dinie: Still follows her routine of living between Spain and Holland.

Vincente and Lynda: Still live in Spain, near us. We can hear his Meow from our house.

Juan: Still visits the salon and is always there waiting. Every wife should have an admirer in their life; it keeps the husbands on their toes.

Louis: Lives in England as a successful carpenter.

Sarina: Still lives in Spain, now has a successful stickers business. Her favourite program is The Apprentice. She is now growing into an intelligent well-mannered young woman. We no longer call her Chucky.

Jo and Michael: Still struggle living together, only love keeps them there.

Barclay: Still lives with us and comes to work each day, so he's out of Michael's way!

Authors note

If ever you're on the Costa Blanca and you can hear an Essex girl singing in a bar, 'It's raining men', that's me.